# Getting on Track With APRS

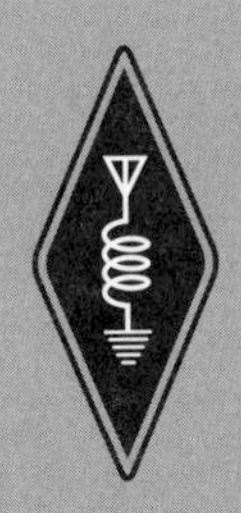

**A Hands-On Guide to the Automatic Packet Reporting System**

By Stan Horzepa, WA1LOU

Published by: **The American Radio Relay League**
225 Main Street, Newington, CT 06111-1494

Printed in USA



First Edition

ISBN: 0-87259-585-4

# Contents

# Foreword

APRS, the Automatic Packet Reporting System, is an exciting new mode that integrates packet radio, mapping graphics and the Global Positioning System (GPS) into a single program. A number of things had to take place to make APRS possible.

First, and most important, the amateur community must thank Bob Bruninga, WB4APR, for having shared his professional APRS endeavors with us.

Second, the Sproul brothers created Mac and Windows versions of Bob's program.

Third, GPS prices fell to a point where amateurs could afford them.

The result has been nothing short of phenomenal: a whole new, low-cost mode of operation has evolved. If you are already on packet radio and have a PC, you can try APRS for free because the programs are offered as shareware.

The purpose of this book is to make it as effortless as possible to get on APRS. Detailed step-by-step instructions are given for DOS, Mac and Windows users. Why not give this new mode a try? Who knows—you might end up tracking the flight of a balloon or the path of a sailboat as it crosses the ocean. Closer to home, it can add a new dimension to your public-service activities by tracking participants in real time.

No matter what applications you find for APRS, you'll find it an exciting new way of using packet radio technology.

David Sumner, K1ZZ
Executive Vice President
December 1996

# Preface

APRS is the abbreviation for Automatic Packet/Position Reporting System, an integration of software and hardware that has become the latest application to take the packet radio world by storm (like the *WØRLI Mailbox*, *NET/ROM*, *NOS* and the *DX PacketCluster* applications before it).

APRS allows you to track real-time events using packet radio. This in itself, is a valuable communications tool. But what makes APRS even more useful is its ability to represent real-time events graphically. Rather than staring at monotonous lines of scrolling text, you can watch events unfold on detailed maps right on your computer monitor!

The intention of this book is to get you up and running with APRS as quickly and painlessly as possible. By the time you've read it, you will be on your way to becoming a proficient APRS user no matter which version of APRS you use. All three current versions are covered: those for DOS, Macintosh and Windows (specifically, APRS version 7.9.6 for DOS, MacAPRS version 3.0.1 and WinAPRS version 2.0.1).

The "official" name of the DOS version is "APRS." To avoid confusion, however, I use "APRSdos," "MacAPRS" or "WinAPRS" when I write about specific versions of APRS, and I use "APRS" when I refer to something that applies to all three versions.

And finally, note that APRS is a registered trademark of Bob Bruninga, WB4APR, and that Bob also holds copyrights on the APRS protocols.

I hope you enjoy APRS as much as I've enjoyed writing about it!

# Dedication

This book is dedicated to my sister Jeanette Elizabeth "Gigi" Horzepa, who is living proof that blood is thicker than water, fluoridated or otherwise.

# Acknowledgments

Thanks are due the following for their thorough and timely review of the manuscript: Bob Bruninga, WB4APR; Mark Sproul, KB2ICI; and Keith Sproul, WU2Z.

CHAPTER 1

# What is APRS?

The purpose of APRS is to apply packet radio to real-time events especially where information must be relayed quickly. APRS accomplishes this graphically by displaying real-time information on maps that appear on your computer screen, as illustrated in Figure 1-1.

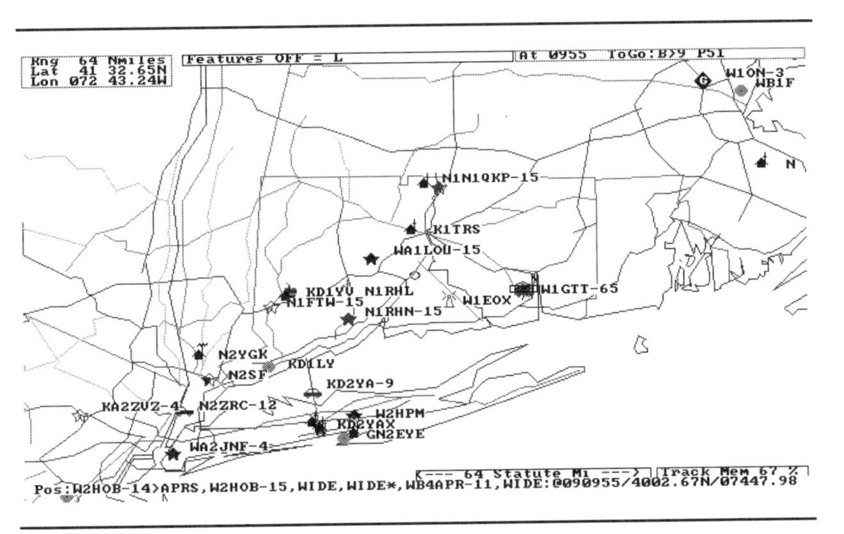


**Figure 1-1—APRS graphically represents real-time events on maps displayed by your computer monitor.**

## APRS has Many Uses

APRS is many things to many people. There are far more uses today than even the originator of APRS conceived of. APRS can be used for:

Tracking vehicles
Fox hunts
Tracking down jammers or other RF interference
Bike-a-thons
Weather tracking
Just for fun
Emergency coordination
Tracking boats in a race
Tracking emergency vehicles such as fire and ambulance
Seeing where you are while driving cross country

APRS communicates using unconnected packets <unnumbered information or UI frames> which contain the station's position, status and any messages. The position packets contain the latitude, longitude, and the station type of the transmitting station. Stations might be homes, portables, mobiles, digipeaters, weather stations, etc. APRS receives these packets, processes the information contained therein and displays an appropriate symbol on a map showing the location of the station. If a station such as a mobile or portable station is in motion, APRS changes the position of that station on the map when it receives new position packets indicating a change of location.

The station in motion may consist of a radio, TNC, and laptop computer running APRS. As that station travels along its intended route, the operator of that station updates the position of the station on the APRS map and APRS relays the new position to all other APRS stations on frequency to update the position of the station on their APRS maps.

On the other hand, the station in motion may consist of a radio, TNC, and a Global Positioning System (GPS) device. The GPS receives signals from Earth-orbiting satellites to calculate its location and periodically sends that information to the TNC of the station in motion, which relays it via radio to the other APRS stations on frequency in order to update the position of the moving station on their APRS maps.

Consider placing a portable APRS station in an emergency vehicle being used in a disaster area or in the lead car of a parade, and the possibility of using APRS as a public service tool becomes obvious.

In addition to tracking Amateur Radio stations in motion, APRS is also able to track any object in motion when the position of that object is entered into the system. For example, you can enter the latitude and longitude of a hurricane along with its station type, which in this case would be hurricane and the position of the hurricane appears on the map of everyone using APRS on that channel.

The public service potential of APRS has no bounds.

CHAPTER 2

# History of APRS

Bob Bruninga, WB4APR, is the father of APRS. Ever since the beginnings of packet radio in the late 1970's, Bob wrote software that combined the flexibility of packet radio with the dynamics of real-time events. Bob designed software based on his observations that communications for most real-time events spend more time concerned with where things are and where they are going than any other single identifiable category. Having served 20 years as a Navy Combat Systems officer, he has considerable experience in tactical networks display and communications.

Bob's years of toiling at a variety of computer keyboards came to a climax when he finished developing the first version of APRSdos in 1992. Since the initial release of APRSdos, Bob has continually worked to improve the software and has added many of the features that were on the wish-lists of its many users. Seven major releases of APRSdos later and Bob is still enhancing the software and new interim releases seem to arrive on a monthly basis.

As Bob nurtured APRSdos, twin brothers and Macintosh

aficionados, Keith and Mark Sproul, WU2Z and KB2ICI respectively, began writing a Macintosh version of APRS. And, in 1994 they released the first version of MacAPRS to the software-starved ham radio members of the Macintosh world.

As Keith and Mark fine-tuned MacAPRS, many DOS users saw the light and decided that the look and feel of the Macintosh operating system was the way to go. However, most were loath to switch computer hardware, so they switched operating systems instead; they switched to Windows, an operating system that attempted to emulate the look and feel of the Macintosh operating system.

Responding to this switch from DOS to Macintosh-emulation in DOS, Mark and Keith began porting MacAPRS to Windows and in 1996, they released MacAPRS for Windows, also known as WinAPRS, for short. As this book goes to press, there is talk of versions of APRS for other computer platforms coming in the near future.

Meanwhile, as Bob, Keith, and Mark cranked out new versions of APRS, its popularity in ham radio grew, and in response, TNC manufacturers began releasing new versions of TNCs that support APRS to one degree or another.

The future of APRS is very bright. With the support of the manufacturers of APRS hardware and the efforts of Bob, Mark, and Keith, the APRS user base and APRS usage should continue to expand into the next century.

CHAPTER 3

# Hardware

Before you can use APRS, you must put together an APRS station. To do this, you must assemble and install the hardware and software that comprise an APRS station. This chapter deals with the hardware, and the following chapter deals with the software.

Basic APRS operation requires the same equipment that you typically use to operate a plain vanilla packet-radio station; that is, a TNC, radio and computer. Advanced APRS operation requires more. This chapter discusses each piece of hardware and how to interconnect all the pieces in order to set up your APRS station.

## TNC Requirements

Any TNC that is compatible with the original TAPR TNC-2 design is also compatible with APRS. Virtually every new TNC sold since 1985 falls into this category, so you should not have any problem finding a suitable TNC for basic APRS operation. However, beyond basic APRS operation, you might need more in your TNC than just TNC-2 compatibility.

## GPS Compatibility

If you plan to use a GPS unit in your APRS operations, there are a number of options available for doing so. First, there are four options if you will be using a portable computer running APRS. With these four options, you can use any TNC-2 compatible TNC.

1. If the computer running APRS has two serial ports, you may use one for connection to your TNC and the other for connection to your GPS unit.

2. If the computer running APRS has one serial port, you may connect a switch to the port and connect your TNC and GPS unit to the switch. Normally, the switch connects the computer and TNC. Whenever you wish to access the GPS unit for position information, however, you use the switch to momentarily connect the computer and GPS unit.

3. If the computer running APRS has one serial port, you may also connect a simple automatic switching circuit (a "hardware single port" switch) to the port and connect your TNC and GPS unit to the switch. Normally, the switching circuit connects the computer and TNC. Whenever APRS wishes to access the GPS unit for position information, however, it automatically switches the circuit to momentarily connect the computer and GPS unit.

4. If the computer running APRS has one serial port and the GPS unit has user-programmable periodicity, you may connect your TNC and GPS unit to the serial port via a simple diode OR circuit and program the GPS unit to send position information on a one minute basis.

For operators using GPS as a "stand-alone tracker," where there will be no portable computer running APRS, there is a new breed of TNC available that adds options for GPS operation. These TNCs have added support for GPS operation, so if your TNC is compatible with that firmware release, you may connect your GPS unit to the serial port of the TNC. In this set up, your station only broadcasts GPS position information over the air to other APRS stations. There is no computer running APRS connected to your TNC.

Recognizing the need to rapidly reconfigure between stand-alone and laptop operation, some TNCs even provide a second serial port for GPS operation. As a result, you may use one serial port for connection to your GPS unit and the other for connection to a computer running APRS.

## APRS Compatibility

Traditionally TNC-2 compatibles could be programmed with your call sign (via the **MYCall** command) and with a second alternative identification (via the **MYAlias** command). In some APRS applications, like wide-area digipeater operations, it is advantageous to be able to program your TNC with two alternative identifications.

Although there are ways of accomplishing this with many TNCs, now there are TNCs that truly support multiple alternative identifications. So, if you are shopping for a new TNC (especially if you are shopping for a new one for APRS), seriously consider buying one that provides multiple alternative identification support. It is worth noting that PacComm, which sells TNCs with multiple alternative identification support, also sells firmware for non-PacComm TNCs that includes multiple alternative identification support.

## Single or Dual Port Operation

Some TNCs are available with separate modems for VHF/UHF and HF applications. Separate VHF/UHF and HF radio ports permit the simultaneous connection of VHF and HF radio equipment and this is the type of TNC you need for dual-port or gateway APRS applications.

## Computer Requirements

In plain vanilla packet-radio applications, you do not need a computer to communicate with your TNC. Most of the time you can get by using a dedicated terminal (terminal or DTE, for short), which is a device that is designed for the single purpose of communicating with computers, typically mainframe computer systems in corporate, educational, and governmental environments.

APRS is not a plain vanilla application. It is software and as such, requires a computer. The DOS, Macintosh, and Windows versions of APRS run on computers of the DOS, Macintosh, and Windows ilk, and each version of APRS has minimum computer requirements. These requirements are specified in the following paragraphs.

### APRSdos

APRSdos runs on DOS computers using the 8088 microprocessor to those using the Pentium microprocessor (and beyond). It requires 540 kbytes of RAM. It is compatible with CGA, EGA, and VGA video, but requires a standard video card (non-standard video cards like the Hercules video card do not work).

### MacAPRS (Macintosh Version)

MacAPRS, the Macintosh version of APRS, runs on Macintosh computers using System 7.0 or later. It requires a minimum of 4 Mbytes of RAM. A color monitor is recommended and multiple monitors are supported.

Note that there are two versions of MacAPRS. One for Macintosh computers using a 68xxx microprocessor and another for Macintosh computers using the Power PC microprocessor. The PowerPC version has a suffix of ppc appended to its compressed and BinHexed file name.

### WinAPRS (Windows Version)

WinAPRS, the Windows version of APRS, runs on any computer using Windows 95 or Windows NT. It also runs on any computer using Windows 3.1, but requires the installation of the Win32s library (DLL) in a Windows 3.1 computer. A Windows 95/NT computer with a 33-MHz 486 microprocessor (or better) and 8 Mbytes of RAM is recommended, although it may work with as little as 4 Mbytes.

## Radio Equipment Requirements

APRS does not require any special radio equipment. If your Amateur Radio station performs well with plain vanilla packet-radio applications, then it should perform well with APRS.

Of course, the radio equipment must be capable of transmitting and receiving signals on the bands you intend to operate. With this in mind, you need radio equipment that operates on two radio bands if you intend to operate a dual-port or gateway APRS station. This scenario typically requires HF radio equipment and VHF or UHF radio equipment.

## GPS

The APRS requirement for GPS equipment is simple. Any GPS equipment that outputs data in NMEA (National Marine Electronics Association) format will work with APRS. In fact, any navigational equipment (such as LORAN) that outputs data in NMEA format will also work with APRS. Note that aeronautical GPS equipment does not output NMEA formatted data.

Once you meet the NMEA data format requirement, it is your choice as to what kind of GPS equipment to purchase. For mobile and portable APRS applications, the size, weight and power requirements of the GPS unit should be considered. The smaller the better should be your goal. A GPS unit that fits in a TNC would do nicely.

Another consideration for mobile and portable applications are the antenna options of the GPS unit. With APRS GPS applications, you now have to worry about two antennas, one for your radio equipment and one for the GPS unit. Again, the smaller the better should be your goal. A GPS unit with a self-contained antenna is your best choice, but access to an external antenna jack is highly desirable.

## Weather Station

All three versions accept data from the Peet Bros. Ultimeter-II, Peet Bros. U-2000, WeatherMAX and Davis Weather Monitor home weather stations. In addition, the Macintosh and Windows versions of APRS also accept data from the Heathkit 5001 home weather station.

## Hardware Interconnections

The hardware interconnections of a basic APRS packet-radio station are straightforward. You connect your TNC to your computer and radio equipment in the same manner as you would for a plain vanilla packet radio.

The hardware interconnections of auxiliary APRS equipment, such as a GPS unit or weather station, is similarly straightforward. You connect the auxiliary equipment to your computer in a manner similar to the way you connect your TNC to your computer.

### TNC-to-Computer Connection

Most TNCs are designed to be connected to a computer by means of a serial port that is compatible with EIA standards EIA-232. In most cases, a 9 or 25-pin subminiature D-type connector provides the physical connection to your TNC. If your computer also has an EIA-compatible interface, the connection is accomplished by means of a 9 or 25-wire cable

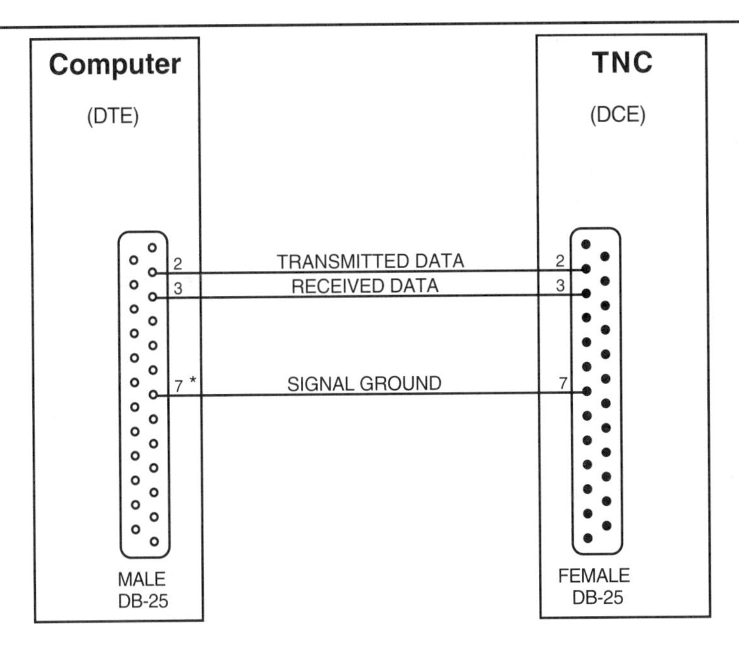


**Figure 3-1—The minimal TNC-to-computer interconnection requires only three wires.**

with the appropriate connectors at each end. "Appropriate" refers to connector gender. According to industry standards, a DTE has a male connector on its serial port while a DCE has a female connector. The DTE in this case is your computer and the DCE is your TNC. This means that an appropriate cable has a male connector at the TNC end and a female connector at the computer end. This standard is not always adhered to, however.

Cables containing all 25 wires are expensive. All 25 pins of the EIA-232 interface are not used by your TNC. APRS uses only three pins. Interconnections between pins 2 (Transmitted Data), 3 (Received Data), and 7 (Signal Ground) are adequate for almost all applications. A 3-wire cable is certainly less expensive than a 25-wire cable. Figure 3-1 illustrates the TNC-to-terminal interconnection.

Even less expensive is not needing a cable at all! If you already have a cable connecting your computer to a telephone line modem, it is very likely that you can use that same cable to connect your computer to your TNC.

## Auxiliary APRS Equipment Connections

Typically, auxiliary APRS devices, such as weather station and NMEA equipment, use a serial port interface that is similar to or exactly like the one used between your TNC and computer, that is, EIA-232. NMEA equipment uses an EIA-422 interface, but it may be connected to an EIA-232 interface in most cases without difficulty.

In most auxiliary APRS equipment applications, APRS

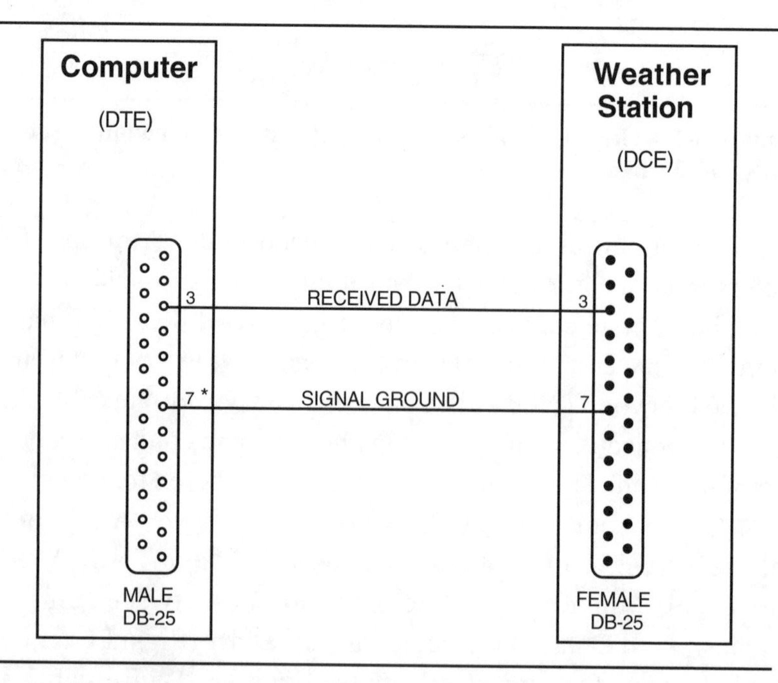


**Figure 3-2—Usually, only two signals are needed to interface a computer and weather station.**

only needs to receive data from the auxiliary equipment. As a result, the interconnection between the auxiliary equipment and APRS computer requires only two wires, one to connect grounds and one to connect the output of the auxiliary equipment to the input of the computer serial port (Received Data). Figure 3-2 illustrates the interface between a computer and a weather station, while Figure 3-3 illustrates the interface

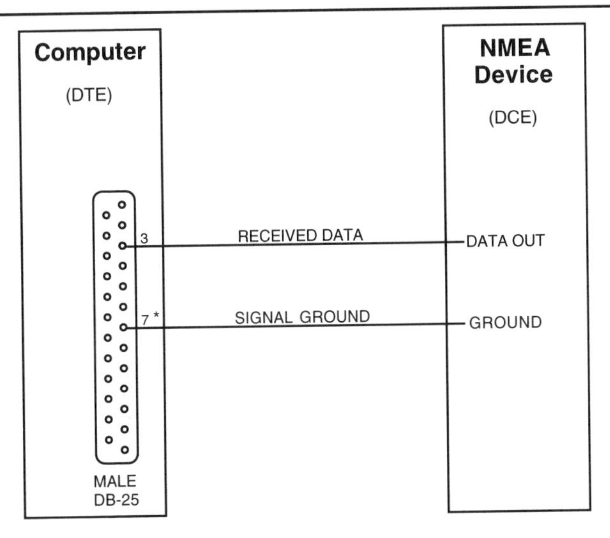


If the 2-wire connection does not work, try the following:

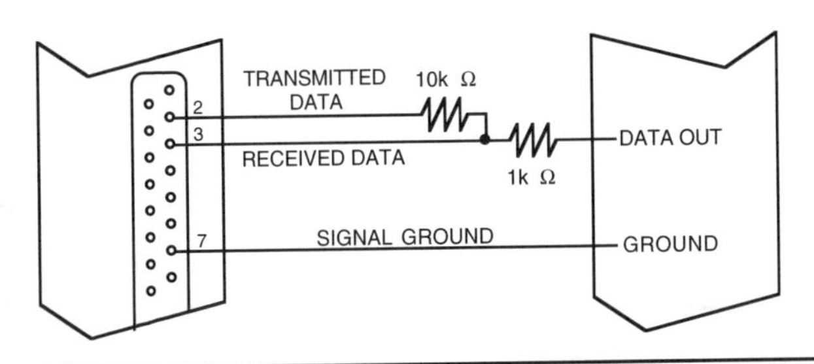


**Figure 3-3—The successful interfacing of an NMEA device to a computer requires two, maybe three signal connections.**

between a computer and an NMEA device. Note that these are typical, maybe ideal examples of auxiliary equipment interfacing. Check the documentation that accompanies the auxiliary equipment for any curves.

### *GPS Interconnection Options*

There are a variety of options available for interconnecting your GPS unit to your computer and TNC. These options are dependent on the features of the computer and TNC, as described earlier in this chapter (refer to the paragraphs under "GPS Compatibility"). Figures 3-4 through 3-7 illustrate the various options that are available today.

## TNC-to-Radio Equipment Connection

In most cases, interfacing your TNC to your radio equipment is a matter of making a few simple connections.

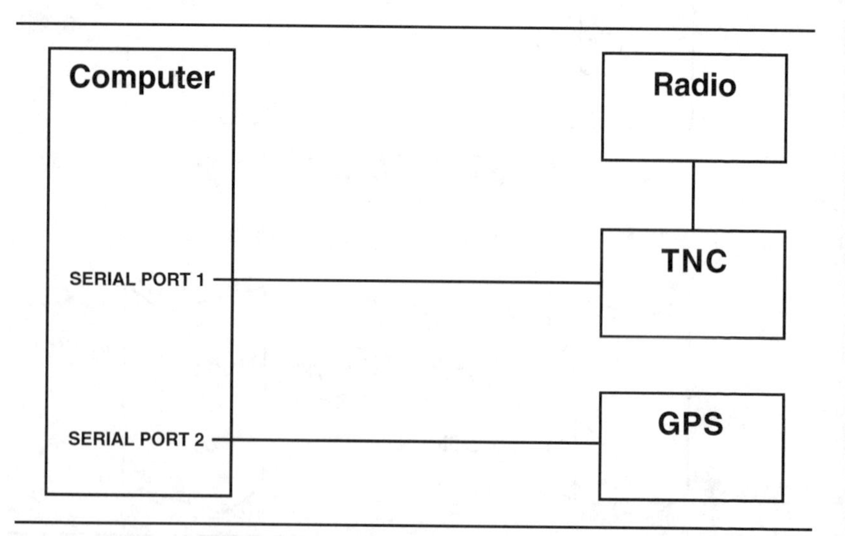


**Figure 3-4—Connecting a GPS unit to a computer with two serial ports is easy.**

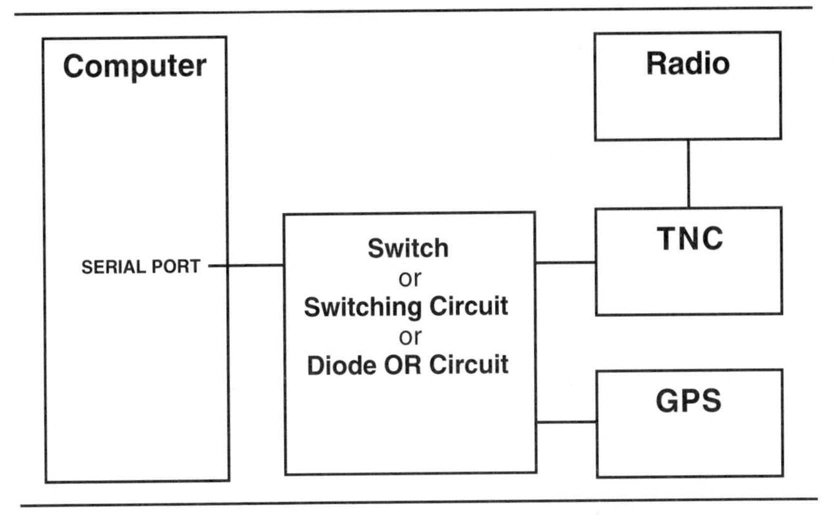


**Figure 3-5—Connecting a GPS unit to a computer with only one serial port requires a simple interface.**

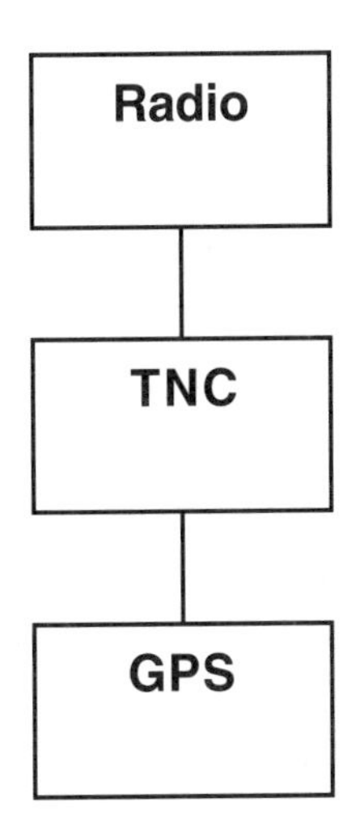


**Figure 3-6—GPS-compatible TNCs make GPS tracking possible without a computer.**

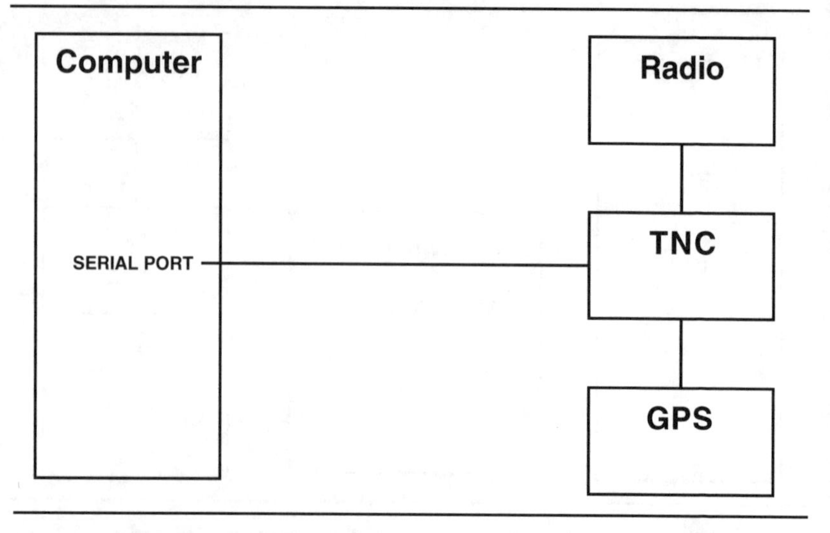


**Figure 3-7—A computer with only one serial port can run APRS with GPS when the GPS-compatible TNC provides a second port for the GPS connection.**

Figure 3-8 illustrates the TNC-to-radio interconnection.

The audio output of the TNC is connected to the audio input of your transmitter/transceiver. Typically, the audio input of your radio equipment is a microphone connector, but some transceivers have separate audio inputs for AFSK tones (sometimes labeled "AFSK in"). If such a connection is available, it's better to use that connection rather than the microphone input because you will not have to disconnect the packet-radio equipment whenever you want to use the radio in the voice mode. In addition, the transceiver may have circuitry that processes the AFSK input signals in some way and such processing would probably be beneficial to your packet-radio signal as well.

The push-to-talk (PTT) line from your TNC is connected to a PTT connection on your transmitter/transceiver. Usually, PTT is available at the microphone connector, but the PTT line

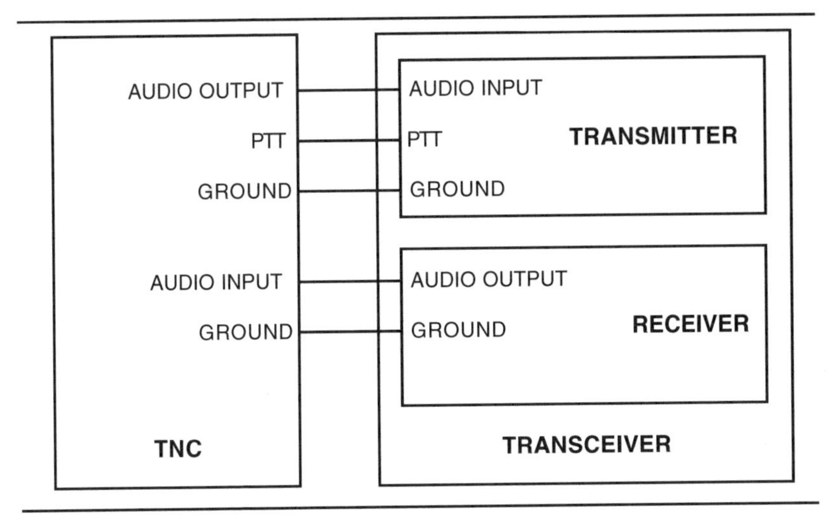


**Figure 3-8—Most TNC-to-radio interconnections look like this.**

is sometimes brought out to another jack as well. Again, connection to the optional PTT jack is preferable; this avoids cable changes when you switch modes.

The audio output of your receiver/transceiver is connected to the audio input of your TNC. Typically, the audio output of your radio is a speaker or headphone connector, but some radios have optional audio outputs (sometimes labeled "AFSK out"). Again, connection to such an optional audio output avoids cable changes and the receiver/transceiver may provide some filtering or processing of the AFSK output signals. If your radio does not have separate AFSK jacks, the phone patch input and output jacks often provide an acceptable alternative.

In addition to these three connections, there must be a ground connection between your TNC and the transceiver (or transmitter and receiver).

Dual-port TNCs provide two sets of connections. Using the same procedures described above, you connect one set of connections to the radio equipment intended for one port of the

TNC and connect the other set to the radio equipment intended for the other port of the TNC.

Some transmitters/transceivers, typically VHF and UHF hand-held transceivers, use a common conductor for audio input and PTT. Simply connecting the TNC audio output and PTT leads to the common conductor on the radio will not work. To make the connection successfully, a capacitor and resistor are often required in the wiring circuit. Consult the manual that accompanies your radio for what is required to complete this connection.

## RFI Prevention

To prevent radio frequency interference (RFI), all cables should be shielded. If shielding does not prevent RFI, all cables including all ac line cables, should be wound around a toroid.

CHAPTER 4

# Software

All the hardware that you use for APRS existed before APRS was created. Without APRS software, the hardware could be used in a variety of plain vanilla packet-radio applications. With APRS software, the hardware becomes APRS hardware. This chapter explains how to transform that plain vanilla packet-radio hardware into APRS hardware.

## Preliminaries

There are a few preliminary steps you need to take before you can begin the transformation.

### Obtaining Your Station Coordinates

As they say in the real estate business, what is important is "location, location, location." The same can be said for APRS. In order for APRS to operate as accurately as possible, you need to know your exact location and program the APRS software with that information.

A city, town, or street address is not accurate enough. What you need is your station coordinates, that is, the latitude and longitude of your APRS station, preferably in degrees, minutes, and seconds. There are a few ways to obtain this information.

The simplest is to just run the software and zoom into the map of your area. The location of the cursor will show the exact latitude and longitude for that position. Of course, this method is only as accurate as the level of detail included in the APRS maps. Usually this accuracy is adequate to get you started. The most accurate, but most expensive, way to obtain your station coordinates is by using a GPS unit that provides that information. If you know someone who has a GPS unit and is willing to help you out, then you have a substantial economic savings without forgoing the ease and accuracy. If you purchased a GPS unit to use with APRS, then you have it made. However, I would not advise purchasing a GPS unit just to obtain your station coordinates for the sake of APRS accuracy. There are less expensive and still accurate ways of determining your coordinates.

You can look it up. Using a good map of your area, you can determine your coordinates with fairly good accuracy. Topographic maps like the 7.5 minute quadrangles published by the United States Geological Survey (USGS, Washington, DC 20242) are perfect for determining your coordinates. The USGS maps are inexpensive and very detailed. If you don't live in an urban area, the building that houses your APRS station likely appears on the USGS quadrangle for your area. So, that should permit you to determine your coordinates fairly accurately.

You can also look up your coordinates in an atlas. The maps in an atlas are not usually as detailed as the USGS quadrangles, so determining your coordinates using a map in an atlas produces less accurate results. You can use those results as a starting point and fine tune them later, however.

Some atlases list all the major cities and towns in the world and sometimes the latitude and longitude of each city and town. Some almanacs provide similar lists, but only for the major cities. The accuracy of such lists varies depending on how close you live to the location in your town or city where the coordinates were determined. If you live over the town hall or post office, you are in pretty good shape using the coordinates from an atlas or almanac. If you live on the back forty of Old MacDonald's farm, the coordinates may be off a bit.

If you are on the Internet, you can obtain your coordinates from the Geographic Name Server run by the Regents of the University of Michigan. Simply **telnet://martini.eecs.umich.edu:3000/** and after the server start-up message appears, enter your location. In a few seconds, the server provides you with a variety of information concerning your location including its latitude and longitude in degrees, minutes, and seconds. For example, when I entered Wolcott, CT, the server responded with the following:

```
0 Wolcott
1 09009 New Haven
2 CT Connecticut
3 US United States
A 203
F 45 Populated place
L 41 36 08 N 72 59 14 W
Z 06716
```

If you do not have telnet capabilities, use a Web browser and surf to **http://www.geocode.com/eagle.html-ssi**, where you enter your station address (street, city, state, ZIP code) and receive your station coordinates in return.

## Obtaining the Software

The most important thing you need to use APRS is APRS!

The programs come bundled with some demo map files. Luckily, it is fairly easy to get the software and map files. For starters, you can obtain the various flavors of APRS software and map files from the usual sources, including Amateur Radio oriented telephone bulletin board systems like the ARRL BBS (phone 860 594-0306) or from Amateur Radio interest groups of on-line services like CompuServe, America Online and GEnie.

To ftp the APRS software and map files, there are two sites that always have the latest versions of APRS and plenty of maps.

**ftp.tapr.org** is one site. In subdirectory **/tapr/SIG/aprssig/files**, look in the appropriate subdirectory, **/dosstuff**, **/macstuff**, or **/winstuff**, for APRSdos, MacAPRS, and WinAPRS, respectively. For maps, in subdirectory **/tapr/SIG/aprssig/files/maps** look in the appropriate subdirectory, **/MacMaps**, **/PCMaps**, and **/WinMacMaps** for MacAPRS, APRSdos, and WinAPRS/MacAPRS maps, respectively.

**aprs.rutgers.edu** is the other site. In subdirectory **/pub/hamradio/APRS**, look in the appropriate subdirectory, **/APRS**, **/MacAPRS**, or **/WinAPRS** for the current versions of APRS software. For maps, in subdirectory **/hamradio/APRS**, look in subdirectories **/100K Maps** and **/DCW Maps** for WinAPRS/MacAPRS maps and in subdirectory **/DOS_Maps** for APRSdos maps.

To get the software and maps on disk or CD-ROM, contact the APRS authors. For APRSdos, contact Bob Bruninga, WB4APR, at 115 Old Farm Ct, Glen Burnie, MD 21060 or at **http://web.usna.navy.mil/~bruninga.aprs.html**. For MacAPRS, contact Keith Sproul, WU2Z, at 698 Magnolia Rd., North Brunswick, NJ 08902 or at **ksproul@noc.rutgers.edu**. For WinAPRS, contact Mark Sproul, KB2ICI, at 698 Magnolia Rd., North Brunswick, NJ 08902 or at **sproul@ap.org**.

You may also contact the authors for help concerning APRS or to join the TAPR APRS Special Interest Group (APRSSIG) where APRS questions and answers, news and views are exchanged continuously. To subscribe to APRSSIG, send e-mail to **listserve@tapr.org** with the following in the body of the message: **subscribe aprssig *Firstname Lastname***. Last, but not least, there is the TAPR Web site (**http://www.tapr.org/tapr/html/sigs.html**), which offers one-stop shopping for APRS. There you can download APRS software and find links to everything associated with all versions of APRS.

### Registering the Software

All flavors of APRS are shareware. Shareware is software that you can try out to see if it is suitable for you. Only if you find it suitable and plan to continue to use it, are you obligated to pay a nominal shareware registration fee to the APRS authors.

Note that unregistered APRS software is not fully functional. The main function that does not work with unregistered APRS software is the ability to save the APRS software configuration (you have to configure the software every time you start it). If you register your APRS software, you receive a registration number that you enter into the software and then it becomes fully functional. (Information on how to register the software is included with each flavor of APRS.)

## APRSdos: Installing and Configuring

After you install the APRS hardware, determine your station coordinates (latitude and longitude), and obtain the

APRS software, you can install APRSdos according to the following steps.

1. Power up your computer.

2 Create a new directory for APRS on your computer hard disk (enter **MD APRS**).

3. If the compressed (zipped) APRS is on a diskette:

a. Change directories to the new APRS directory (enter **CD APRS**).

b. Insert the diskette containing APRS into the A: disk drive.

c. Change drives to the A: disk drive (enter **A:**).

d. Decompress APRS using *PKUNZIP* (enter **PKUNZIP -d <compressed APRS file name> C:**)

4. If the compressed (zipped) APRS is already on your computer hard disk:

a. Change directories to the directory containing the compressed (zipped) APRS (enter **C:/<directory name>**).

b. Decompress APRS using PKUNZIP (enter **PKUNZIP -d <compressed APRS file name> C:/APRS)**.

5. Similarly, use PKUNZIP to unzip any *map.zip* files.

That completes the installation of APRSdos. Now you can configure APRS according to the following steps. Remember, if you have not registered your APRS software, you must configure the software each time you start it.

1. Assuming that your computer is already on, power up the rest of your APRS hardware (TNC and radio equipment).

2. Tune the radio to the local APRS operating frequency (if available in your area, 145.79, 445.925, and 10.1515 MHz are popular APRS operating frequencies), and APRS mode (FM on VHF and UHF, LSB on HF).

3. Start APRS (enter **<APRS file name>**).

4. After the APRS start-up screen appears as illustrated in Figure 4-1, the program prompts you for the following

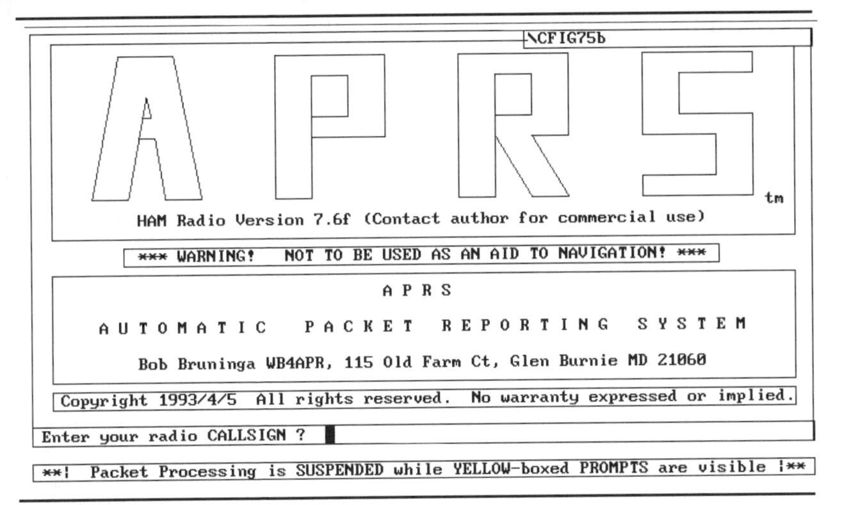


**Figure 4-1—The first time you start up APRSdos, it prompts you for your call sign.**

information:

a. Enter your call sign. Remember to enter an SSID if one is desired.

b. Enter the number of the computer serial (COM) port that is connected to your TNC (COM port 1 is the default selection).

c. Enter the baud rate of the TNC serial port (4800 baud is the default selection).

d. Enter the operating band of the APRS radio equipment, either **HF** or **VHF** (VHF is the default selection). Enter **VHF** for UHF.

e. Enter the type of TNC you are using. The selections are **AEA**, **Dual Pico** (for PacComm PicoPacket), **PacComm** and **OTHER** (for everything else).

f. Enter whether the TNC you are using is a dual band **KAM** (for Kantronics KAM), **AEA PK-900/2232**, or **NEITHER** (for everything). Neither is the default selection.

g. Enter the time used by the computer clock, either **Zulu** (for Greenwich Mean/Universal Time) or **Local** (for local time). Local time is the default selection.

h. If your computer clock uses local time, enter the number of hours your time zone differs from GMT/UTC.

i. Enter the number of the computer serial (COM) port that is connected to other APRS equipment, if any (such as a weather station, direction finding equipment, GPS unit, or LORAN equipment).

j. If another computer serial (COM) port is connected to other APRS equipment, then the program prompts you for additional information concerning that equipment; otherwise, this is the end of prompting for configuration information.

5. After the map of the United States appears, you should select the list of maps that is appropriate for your region. Do this by entering **M** (for Maps), then **C** (for Change). When prompted, enter the appropriate extension for your region, either **EAS**, **NEA**, **CEN**, **WES**, or **SE** for the eastern, northeastern, central, western, and southeastern United States respectively.

6. If you know your station coordinates, skip to step 7. If you do not know your station coordinates, use the computer mouse or arrow keys to move the cursor to your approximate location on the map. Use the **Page Down** key as many times as necessary to magnify the map to permit you to more accurately position the cursor on your location. Holding the cursor key will zoom by a factor of eight. When you believe that the cursor is positioned on your location, go to step 7 and respond to the prompts appropriately.

7. Enter **I** (for Input) and **M** (for My), and **P** (for Position).

a. The software will prompt you with the current coordinates of the cursor. If your location is different, enter your latitude in the following format: DDMM.HHC, where DD is degrees, MM is minutes, HH is hundredths of a minute, and C is direction (N, S, E, or W). For example, if your latitude is 41° 37' 30" North, enter **4137.50N**. Note the APRS standard is to use decimal 100ths of a minute instead of seconds. To convert seconds to hundredths, simply divide the seconds by 60.

b. Similarly, enter your longitude in the following format: DDDMM.HHC, where DDD is degrees, MM is minutes, HH is hundredths of a minute, and C is direction (N, S, E, or W). For example, if your longitude is 72° 56' 45" West, enter **07256.75W**. Remember to enter leading zero(s) for longitudes less than 100°. (By the way, if your station coordinates are 41° 37' 30" North and 72° 56' 45" West, get out of my attic!)

c. When prompted, select a symbol to represent your station on the map. There is a large selection of symbols to choose from and there is likely to be one that fits your needs. Assuming your station is located in your home, enter **B** (for Buildings), then **Q** (for QTH), and a house with an antenna is the map symbol for your station.

d. Again, assuming your station is located in your home and your home is not moving, ignore the next two prompts concerning course and speed (just press the **Return** key in response to each prompt).

e. The next prompt permits you to input a comment that the program appends to each APRS position packet that it transmits. The comment can be related to your name, location, or whatever you feel is appropriate. If you don't know what you want at this time, you can always use the **I** and **M** commands later to add a comment after you see what other stations on the air are using for comments.

f. Press the **Enter** key at the **Enter DAY-TIME (DDHHMM)** prompt.

g. The last prompt asks you to confirm (yes or no)

the information you have just entered.

8. Enter your status beacon using **I** (for Input), **M** (for My) and **S** (for Status). For mobiles or actual real time events, your status beacon informs others of your current situation and/or activities.

9. Next enter the radio range information about your station by entering **I** (for Input) and **P** (for Power-Height-Gain).

a. When prompted, enter your transmitter power. The maximum entry in this field is 81 watts. Entering anything larger than 81 results in 81. The reason for this limitation is to promote the use of minimum power in APRS networks.

b. When prompted, enter the Height Above Average Terrain (HAAT). HAAT is not the same as your height above sea level. HAAT is the height of your antenna as it relates to the average height of the terrain in a 10-mile radius surrounding the antenna. For example, if your antenna is 1000 feet above sea level and the average terrain in the 10-mile radius surrounding the antenna is 900 feet, your HAAT is 100 feet.

To calculate HAAT, use a topographical map and record

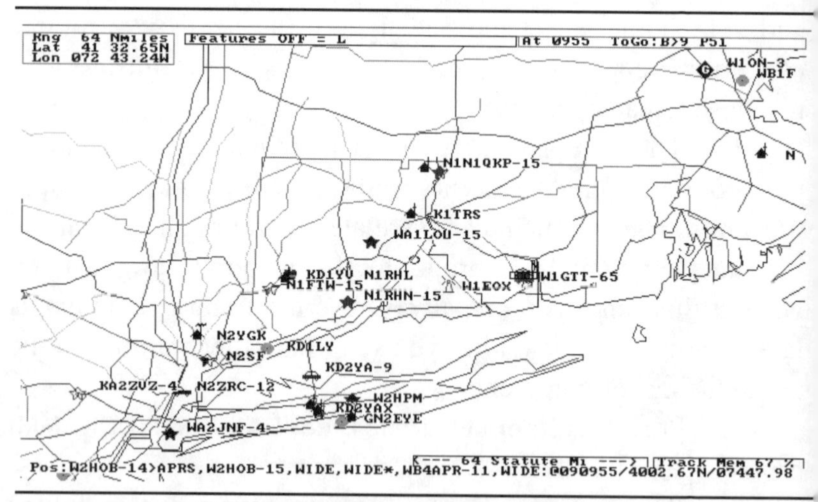


**Figure 4-2—After you configure and run APRSdos for a few minutes, your APRS map looks something like this.**

the height of the terrain in 2-mile increments along the eight compass directions (N, NE, E, SE, S, SW, W, and NW) radiating 10-miles out from your antenna. For example, in the northeast direction, you would record the height of the terrain at the points that are 2, 4, 6, 8, and 10 miles northeast of your antenna. When you are finished, you should have 40 points recorded. Add them together, divide the sum by 40, and subtract the result from the height of your antenna above sea level. The difference is your HAAT.

c. When prompted, enter the gain of your antenna in dB.

d. When prompted, enter the directivity of your antenna. You may enter **0** for an omnidirectional antenna, however, if local terrain affects the operation of your omnidirectional antenna, you may enter a figure that represents the direction that your antenna favors. For example, if a mountain to your west causes your antenna to favor the east, you could enter **90**.

10. Save your APRS configuration. Do this by entering **ALT-S** (press the ALT and S keys at the same time). When prompted, enter your registration validation number. (Avoiding reconfiguration each time you start APRS should be plenty of incentive to register your APRS software.)

That completes the initial installation and configuration of APRS. Once you get a feel for your local APRS network, you can fine tune the configuration especially as it relates to the path your APRS packets use and how your APRS station fits into your local APRS network. Later chapters of the book discuss these issues and how you can manage them to the advantage of your station and your local network.

## MacAPRS (Macintosh Version): Installing and Configuring

After you install the APRS hardware, determine your station coordinates (latitude and longitude), and obtain the

APRS software, you can install the Macintosh version of APRS (known as MacAPRS) according to the following steps.

1. Power up your computer.

2. Create a new folder for MacAPRS on your computer hard disk (select **New Folder** from the **File** menu and enter **MacAPRS**).

3. If the compressed and BinHexed MacAPRS is on a diskette, copy it to your hard disk by selecting the MacAPRS file icon and dragging it into the new MacAPRS folder. If the compressed and BinHexed MacAPRS is already on your computer hard disk, move it into the new MacAPRS folder by selecting the MacAPRS file icon and dragging it into the MacAPRS folder.

4. UnBinHex and decompress the MacAPRS file by using an appropriate version of StuffIt, that is, a version of StuffIt that supports BinHexing/unBinHexing, as well as compression/decompression.

5. Create a new folder for MacAPRS maps on your hard disk (select **New Folder** from the **File** menu and enter **Maps**; note that this folder must be named Maps). Move the new Maps folder into the MacAPRS folder (select the **Maps** folder and drag it into the MacAPRS folder).

6. If the MacAPRS map files are on a diskette, copy them to the new Maps folder by selecting the map file icons and dragging them into the new Maps folder. If the MacAPRS map files are already on your computer hard disk, move them into the new Maps folder by selecting the map file icons and dragging them into the Maps folder.

7. If necessary, unBinHex and/or decompress the map files by using *StuffIt*.

8. Determine which maps you wish to use with MacAPRS. For example, if you live in Connecticut, you may wish to use the CT, Northeast, and USA map files.

9. Determine the order in which you want these maps to open. (The number of maps that can be opened is only limited by the amount of memory that MacAPRS can use.)

10. Add **1.** to the beginning of the file name of the map you wish MacAPRS to open first, **2.** to the beginning of the file name of the map you wish MacAPRS to open second, etc. To do this, select the map file icon and after the map file name is highlighted, place the insertion point at the beginning of the map file name and enter the prefix. For example, if you wanted the CT, Northeast, and USA map files to open in alphabetical order, you would change their file names to **1.CT, 2.Northeast,** and **3.USA**.

That completes the installation of MacAPRS. Now you can configure MacAPRS according to the following steps. Remember, if you have not registered your MacAPRS software, you must configure the software each time you start it.

1. Assuming that your computer is already on, power up the rest of your APRS hardware (TNC and radio equipment).

2. Tune the radio to the local APRS operating frequency (145.79, 445.925, and 10.1515 MHz are the national APRS operating frequencies) and APRS mode (FM on VHF and UHF, LSB on HF).

3. Start MacAPRS (double-click the **MacAPRS** icon).

4. After the MacAPRS start-up screen appears, the program loads the maps you selected in the order you numbered them.

5. If you know your station coordinates, skip to step 7. If you do not know your station coordinates, use the computer mouse to move the pointer to your approximate location on a map. Use the **Page Down** key as many times as necessary to magnify the map to permit you to more accurately position the pointer on your location.

6. When you believe that the pointer is positioned on your location, note the latitude and longitude that appears in the

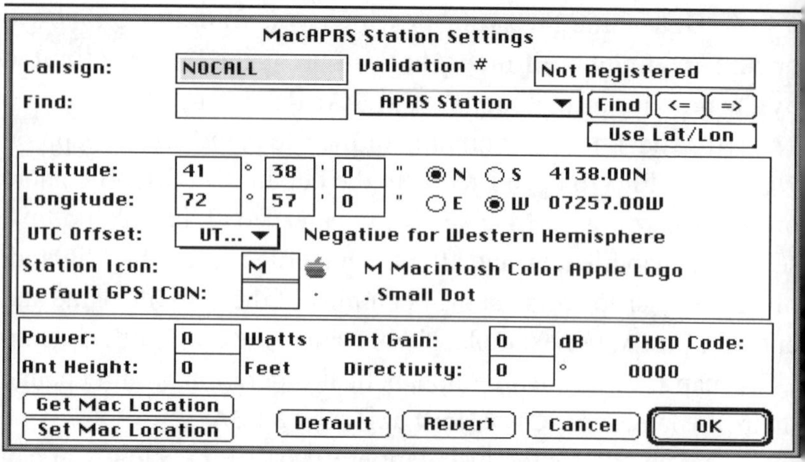

MacAPRS Station Settings

Callsign: NOCALL Validation # Not Registered

Find: APRS Station Find <= =>

Use Lat/Lon

Latitude: 41 ° 38 ' 0 " N S 4138.00N

Longitude: 72 ° 57 ' 0 " E W 07257.00W

UTC Offset: UT... Negative for Western Hemisphere

Station Icon: M M Macintosh Color Apple Logo

Default GPS ICON: . . Small Dot

Power: 0 Watts Ant Gain: 0 dB PHGD Code:

Ant Height: 0 Feet Directivity: 0 ° 0000

Get Mac Location

Set Mac Location Default Revert Cancel OK

**Figure 4-3—The MacAPRS Station Settings window configures the software with your APRS station characteristics.**

lower left corner of the MacAPRS screen. These are your approximate station coordinates.

7. Select **Station Settings...** from the **Settings** menu and enter the following information concerning your station. (Figure 4-3 illustrates the **Station Settings** window.)

a. Enter your call sign in the **Callsign:** box. Remember to enter an SSID if one is desired.

b. Enter your registration number in the **Validation #** box. If your MacAPRS is not registered, you must configure the software each time you start it.

c. Enter your coordinates in the **Latitude:** and **Longitude:** boxes. Select the appropriate compass direction buttons (**N, S, E, W**) for your latitude and longitude.

d. Select the number of hours your time zone differs from GMT/UTC in the **UTC Offset:** menu.

e. The **Station Icon:** box determines the symbol MacAPRS uses to represent your station on the map. The default symbol for MacAPRS is the Apple icon. You can leave his option alone and use the Apple icon or you can choose another icon. There is a large selection of symbols to choose from and there is likely to be one that fits your needs. Assuming your station is located in your home, enter **-** in the **Station Icon:** box and a house with a vertical antenna becomes the map symbol for your station. Enter **y** and a house with a beam antenna is selected.

f. Enter your transmitter power output in the **Power:** box. The maximum entry in this box is 81 watts. Entering anything larger than 81 results in 81. The reason for this limitation is to promote the use of minimum power in APRS networks.

g. Enter the gain of your antenna in the **Ant Gain:** box.

h. Enter the Height Above Average Terrain (HAAT) in the **Ant Height:** box. HAAT is not the same as your height above sea level. HAAT is the height of your antenna as it relates to the average height of the terrain in a 10-mile radius surrounding the antenna. For example, if your antenna is 1000 feet above sea level and the average terrain in the 10-mile radius surrounding the antenna is 900 feet, your HAAT is 100 feet.

To calculate HAAT, use a topographical map and record the height of the terrain in 2-mile increments along the eight compass directions (N, NE, E, SE, S, SW, W, and NW) radiating 10 miles out from your antenna. For example, in the northeast direction, you would record the height of the terrain at the points that are 2, 4, 6, 8, and 10 miles northeast of your antenna. When you are finished, you should have 40 points recorded. Add them together, divide the sum by 40, and subtract the result from the height of your antenna above sea level. The difference is your HAAT.

i. Enter the directivity of your antenna in the **Directivity:** box. You may enter **0** for an omnidirectional antenna, however, if local terrain effects the operation of your omnidirectional antenna, you may enter a figure that represents the direction that your antenna favors. For example, if a mountain to your west causes your antenna to favor the east, you could enter **90** in the **Directivity box:**.

j. Click on the **OK** button.

8. Select **TNC Settings...** from the **Settings** menu and enter

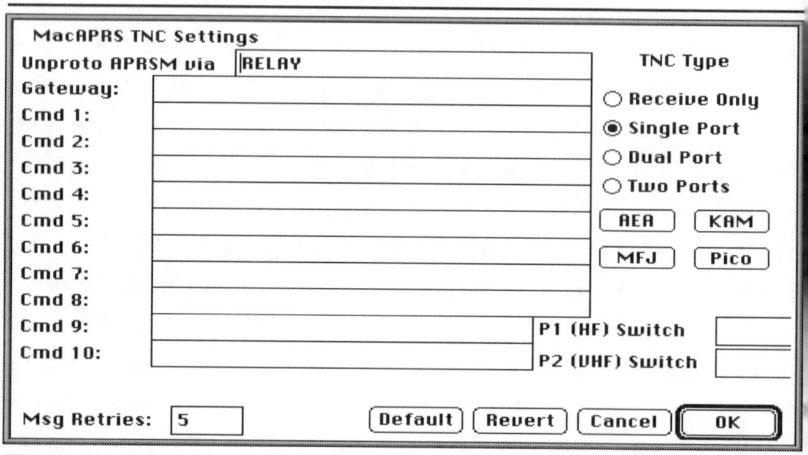

MacAPRS TNC Settings
Unproto APRSM via RELAY
Gateway:
Cmd 1:
Cmd 2:
Cmd 3:
Cmd 4:
Cmd 5:
Cmd 6:
Cmd 7:
Cmd 8:
Cmd 9:
Cmd 10:
TNC Type
Receive Only
Single Port
Dual Port
Two Ports
AEA
KAM
MFJ
Pico
P1 (HF) Switch
P2 (UHF) Switch
Msg Retries: 5
Default
Revert
Cancel
OK

**Figure 4-4—The MacAPRS TNC Settings window configures the software so that it is compatible with the characteristics of your TNC.**

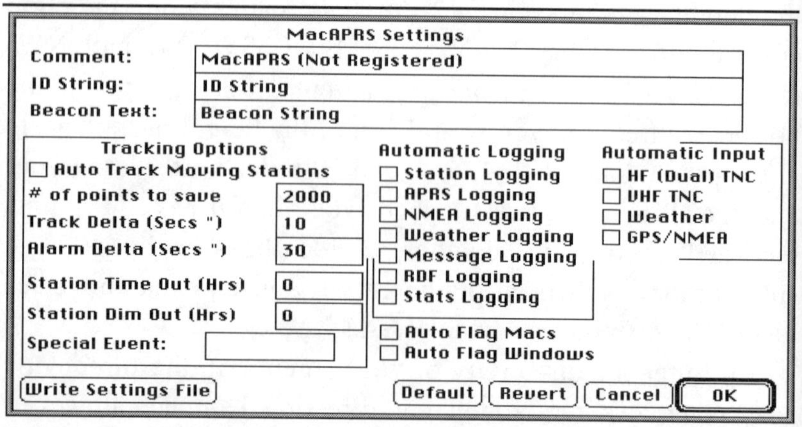

MacAPRS Settings
Comment: MacAPRS (Not Registered)
ID String: ID String
Beacon Text: Beacon String
Tracking Options
Auto Track Moving Stations
# of points to save 2000
Track Delta (Secs ") 10
Alarm Delta (Secs ") 30
Station Time Out (Hrs) 0
Station Dim Out (Hrs) 0
Special Event:
Automatic Logging
Station Logging
APRS Logging
NMEA Logging
Weather Logging
Message Logging
RDF Logging
Stats Logging
Auto Flag Macs
Auto Flag Windows
Automatic Input
HF (Dual) TNC
UHF TNC
Weather
GPS/NMEA
Write Settings File
Default
Revert
Cancel
OK

**Figure 4-5—The MacAPRS Settings window permits you to configure the software with operational parameters of your choosing.**

the following information concerning your TNC. (Figure 4-4 illustrates the **TNC Settings** window.)

a. Under **TNC Type**, click on the appropriate buttons for your TNC: **Receive Only**, **Single Port**, **Dual Port**, **Two Ports**, **AEA**, **KAM** (for Kantronics KAM), **MFJ**, or **Pico** (for PacComm PicoPacket). Depending on your selection(s), MacAPRS loads a set of default commands for your selection(s) in the **Cmd** boxes. These commands are sent to your TNC when you start MacAPRS or when you initialize your TNC from MacAPRS.

b. Click on the **OK** button.

9. Select **MacAPRS Settings...** from the **Settings** menu and enter the following information concerning your station. (Figure 4-5 illustrates the **MacAPRS Settings** window.)

a. In the **Comment:** box, you may enter a comment that the program appends to each APRS position packet that it transmits. The comment can be related to your name, location, or whatever you feel is appropriate. If you don't know what you want at this

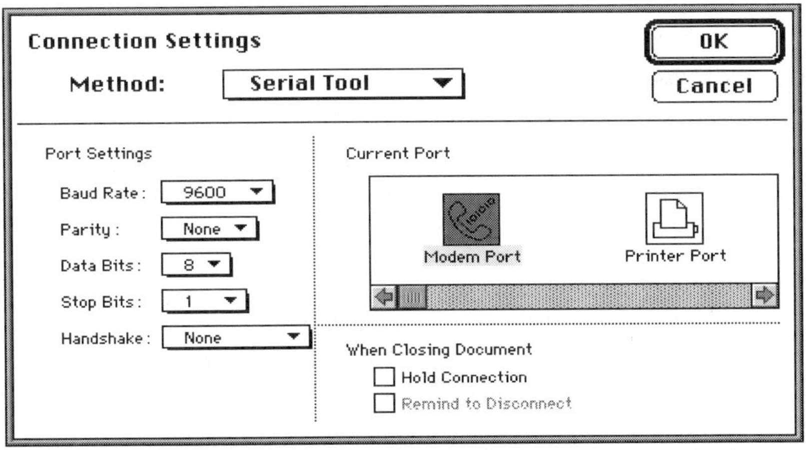

**Figure 4-6—The MacAPRS Connection Settings window configures the software for compatibility with the APRS equipment connected to the serial ports of your computer.**

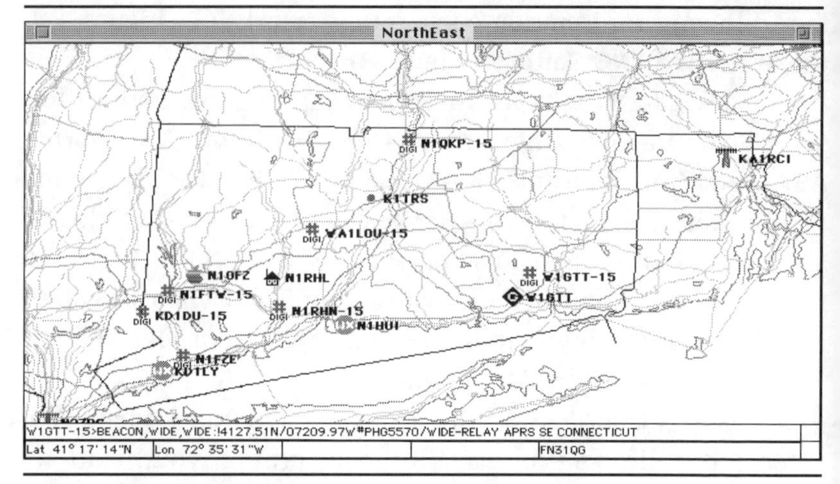


**Figure 4-7—MacAPRS displays what the APRS network looks like on a hot summer night in Southern New England. (Compare it with the Figure 4-2, which display a similar map for APRSdos.)**

time, you can always access **MacAPRS Settings...** later to add a comment after you see what other stations on the air are using.

b. Click on the **OK** button.

10. Select **Communications...** from the **Settings** menu and depending on which band(s) you are using, select **HF** (or **Dual Port**) **TNC** or **VHF TNC**. Select **VHF TNC** for UHF. (Figure 4-6 illustrates the **MacAPRS Settings** window.)

a. Under **Port Settings**, select the operating parameters of the serial port of your TNC from the **Baud Rate:**, **Parity:**, **Data Bits:**, **Stop Bits:**, and **Handshake:** menus.

b. Under **Current Port**, select the computer port your TNC is connected to, either **Modem Port** or **Printer Port.**

c. Click on the **OK** button.

11. If the other computer serial port is connected to other APRS equipment, then select **Communications...** from the **Settings** menu and depending on what other APRS equipment you are using, select **NMEA/GPS**, **Weather**, or **Direction Finding**.

a. Under **Port Settings**, select the operating parameters of the serial port of your other APRS equipment from the **Baud Rate:**, **Parity:**, **Data Bits:**, **Stop Bits:**, and **Handshake:** menus.

b. Under **Current Port**, select the computer port your other APRS equipment is connected to, either **Modem Port** or **Printer Port.**

c. Click on the **OK** button.

12. Depending on which band(s) you are using, select **HF TNC (Dual Port) TNC** or **VHF TNC** from the **Settings** menu. Select **VHF TNC** for UHF. This causes MacAPRS to initialize your TNC with the parameters you have just set in the previous steps. It also causes MacAPRS to begin transmitting, receiving, and displaying APRS information. Figure 4-7 illustrates the appearance of a MacAPRS map after a few hours of APRS network activity

13. You do not have to save your MacAPRS configuration. Each time you clicked on the **OK** button in the various settings windows, MacAPRS saved your settings automatically. (This function is disabled if your software is not registered. Avoiding reconfiguration each time you start MacAPRS should be plenty of incentive to register the software.)

That completes the initial installation and configuration of MacAPRS. Once you get a feel for your local APRS network, you can fine tune the configuration especially as it relates to the path your APRS packets use and how your APRS station fits into your local APRS network. Later chapters of the book discuss these issues and how you can manage them to the advantage of your station and your local network.

## WinAPRS (Windows Version): Installing and Configuring

After you install the APRS hardware, determine your station coordinates (latitude and longitude), and obtain the

APRS software, you can install the Windows version of APRS (known as WinAPRS) according to the following steps.

1. Power up your computer.

2. Create a new directory for WinAPRS on your computer hard disk.

3. Copy the compressed (zipped) WinAPRS into the new WinAPRS directory on your hard disk.

4. Decompress the WinAPRS file by using *WinZip*. The WinAPRS directory should now contain the following files: *winaprs.exe*, *ser16dll.dll*, *serdll32.dll*, *serthunk.dll*, documentation and help files, and the following subdirectories: data, labels, and maps.

5. If maps were bundled with the compressed WinAPRS file, the maps subdirectory contains the maps that WinAPRS uses. If maps were not bundled with the compressed WinAPRS file, you may obtain maps from the same source where you obtained the software. Copy the map files into the maps subdirectory and if they are compressed, decompress them using *WinZip*.

6. Determine which map you wish WinAPRS to use upon start-up. For example, if you live in Connecticut, you may wish to use the New England map file.

7. Rename the map file you wish WinAPRS to use upon start-up so that its new file name begins with the number 1. For example, if you wanted the New England map file to open upon WinAPRS start-up, you change its file name to *1.map*.

That completes the installation of WinAPRS. Now you can configure WinAPRS according to the following steps. Remember, if you have not registered your WinAPRS software, you must configure the software each time you start it.

1. Assuming that your computer is already on, power up the rest of your APRS hardware (TNC and radio equipment).

2. Tune the radio to the local APRS operating frequency

(145.79, 445.925, and 10.1515 MHz are the national APRS operating frequencies) and APRS mode (FM on VHF and UHF, LSB on HF).

3. Start WinAPRS (enter **WINAPRS**).

4. After the WinAPRS start-up screen appears, click on the **OK** button. Select your TNC and its configuration (ports and bands) from the list that appears. Click on the **OK** button. The program begins loading and displays the map you selected for start-up.

5. If you know your station coordinates, skip to step 7. If you do not know your station coordinates, use the computer mouse to move the pointer to your approximate location on a map. Use the **Page Down** key as many times as necessary to magnify the map to permit you to more accurately position the pointer on your location.

6. When you believe that the pointer is positioned on your location, click the mouse button and note the latitude and

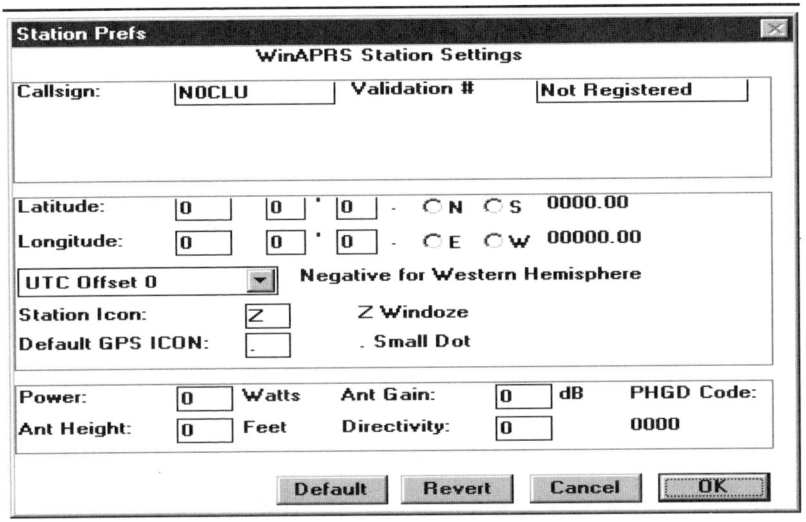

Station Prefs

WinAPRS Station Settings

Callsign: NOCLU    Validation # Not Registered

Latitude: 0 0 ° 0 . N S 0000.00

Longitude: 0 0 ° 0 . E W 00000.00

UTC Offset 0    Negative for Western Hemisphere

Station Icon: Z    Z Windoze

Default GPS ICON: .    . Small Dot

Power: 0 Watts    Ant Gain: 0 dB    PHGD Code:

Ant Height: 0 Feet    Directivity: 0    0000

Default    Revert    Cancel    OK

**Figure 4-8—The WinAPRS Station Settings window programs information about your station into the software.**

longitude that appears at the bottom of the WinAPRS screen. These are your approximate station coordinates.

7. Select **Station** from the **Settings** menu and enter the following information concerning your station in the **WinAPRS Station Settings** window. (Figure 4-8 illustrates the **WinAPRS Station Settings** window.)

a. Enter your call sign in the **Callsign:** box. Remember to enter an SSID if one is desired. The default call sign is **NOCLU.** This is not an actual call sign; it stands for "NO CLUe."

b. Enter your registration number in the **Validation #** box. If your WinAPRS is not registered, you must reconfigure the software each time you start it.

c. Enter your coordinates in the **Latitude:** and **Longitude:** boxes. Select the appropriate compass direction buttons (**N, S, E, W**) for your latitude and longitude.

d. Select the number of hours your time zone differs from GMT/UTC in the **UTC Offset** menu.

e. The **Station Icon:** box determines the symbol WinAPRS uses to represent your station on the map. The default symbol for WinAPRS is the Windows icon. You can leave this option alone and use the Windows icon or you can choose another icon. There is a large selection of symbols to choose from and there is likely to be one that fits your needs. Assuming your station is located in your home, enter - in the **Station Icon:** box and a house with a vertical antenna becomes the map symbol for your station. Enter **y** and a house with a beam antenna is selected.

f. Enter your transmitter power output in the **Power:** box. The maximum entry in this box is 81 watts. Entering anything larger than 81 results in 81. The reason for this limitation is to promote the use of minimum power in APRS networks.

g. Enter the gain of your antenna in the **Ant Gain:** box.

h. Enter the Height Above Average Terrain (HAAT) in

the **Ant Height:** box. HAAT is not the same as your height above sea level. HAAT is the height of your antenna as it relates to the average height of the terrain in a 10-mile radius surrounding the antenna. For example, if your antenna is 1000 feet above sea level and the average terrain in the 10-mile radius surrounding the antenna is 900 feet, your HAAT is 100 feet.

To calculate HAAT, use a topographical map and record the height of the terrain in 2-mile increments along the eight compass directions (N, NE, E, SE, S, SW, W, and NW) radiating 10 miles out from your antenna. For example, in the northeast direction, you would record the height of the terrain at the points that are 2, 4, 6, 8, and 10 miles northeast of your antenna. When you are finished, you should have 40 points recorded. Add them together, divide the sum by 40, and subtract the result from the height of your antenna above sea level. The difference is your HAAT.

i. Enter the directivity of your antenna in the **Directivity:** box. You may enter **0** for an omnidirectional antenna, however, if local terrain effects the operation of your omnidirectional antenna, you may enter a figure that represents the direction that your antenna favors. For example, if a mountain to your west causes your antenna to favor the east, you could enter **90** in the **Directivity** box:.

j. Click on the **OK** button.

8. Select **APRS** from the **Settings** menu and enter the following information concerning your station in the WinAPRS Settings window. (Figure 4-9 illustrates the **WinAPRS Settings** window.)

a. In the **Comment:** box, you may enter a comment that the program appends to each APRS position packet that it transmits. The comment can be related to your name, location, or whatever you feel is appropriate. If you don't know what you want at this time, you can always access APRS from the

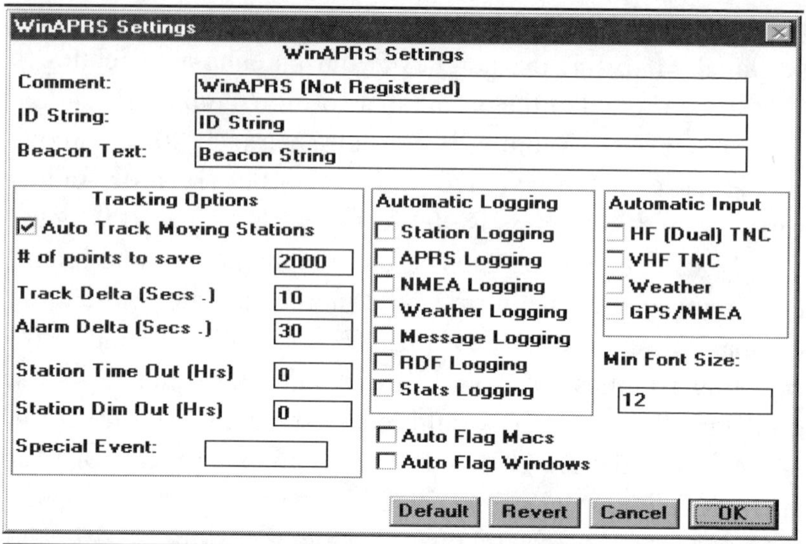

WinAPRS Settings

WinAPRS Settings

Comment: WinAPRS (Not Registered)

ID String: ID String

Beacon Text: Beacon String

Tracking Options

☑ Auto Track Moving Stations

# of points to save: 2000

Track Delta (Secs .): 10

Alarm Delta (Secs .): 30

Station Time Out (Hrs): 0

Station Dim Out (Hrs): 0

Special Event:

Automatic Logging

☐ Station Logging
☐ APRS Logging
☐ NMEA Logging
☐ Weather Logging
☐ Message Logging
☐ RDF Logging
☐ Stats Logging

☐ Auto Flag Macs
☐ Auto Flag Windows

Automatic Input

☐ HF (Dual) TNC
☐ VHF TNC
☐ Weather
☐ GPS/NMEA

Min Font Size: 12

Default | Revert | Cancel | OK

**Figure 4-9—The WinAPRS Settings window allows you to set up the software according to your needs.**

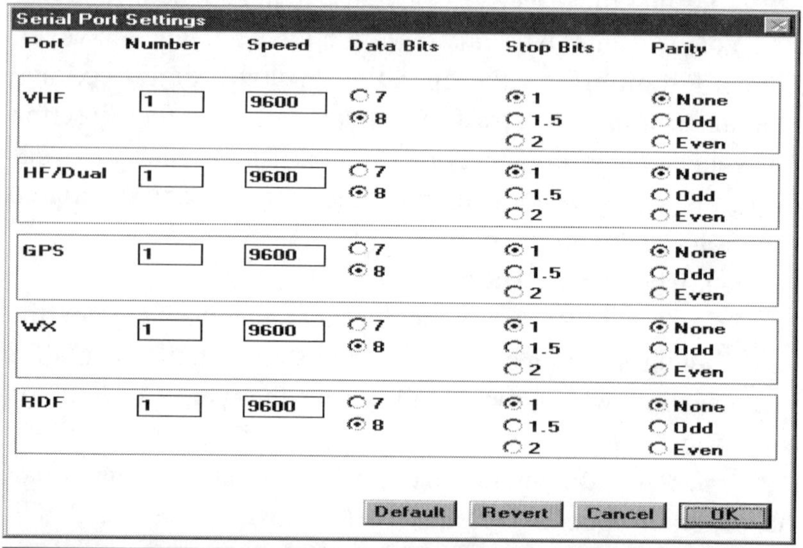

Serial Port Settings

| Port | Number | Speed | Data Bits | Stop Bits | Parity |
|---|---|---|---|---|---|
| VHF | 1 | 9600 | ○ 7 ⦿ 8 | ⦿ 1 ○ 1.5 ○ 2 | ⦿ None ○ Odd ○ Even |
| HF/Dual | 1 | 9600 | ○ 7 ⦿ 8 | ⦿ 1 ○ 1.5 ○ 2 | ⦿ None ○ Odd ○ Even |
| GPS | 1 | 9600 | ○ 7 ⦿ 8 | ⦿ 1 ○ 1.5 ○ 2 | ⦿ None ○ Odd ○ Even |
| WX | 1 | 9600 | ○ 7 ⦿ 8 | ⦿ 1 ○ 1.5 ○ 2 | ⦿ None ○ Odd ○ Even |
| RDF | 1 | 9600 | ○ 7 ⦿ 8 | ⦿ 1 ○ 1.5 ○ 2 | ⦿ None ○ Odd ○ Even |

Default | Revert | Cancel | OK

**Figure 4-10—The Serial Port Settings window configures WinAPRS for compatibility with the APRS equipment connected to the serial ports of your computer.**

**Settings** menu later to add a comment after you see what other stations on the air are using.

b. Click on the **OK** button.

9. Select **Serial Port** from the **Settings** menu. Depending on which band(s) you are using, enter the following information concerning your station in the appropriate box **(HF/Dual Port TNC or VHF TNC**) in the **Serial Port Settings** window. Use the **VHF TNC** box for UHF. (Figure 4-10 illustrates the **Serial Port Settings** window.)

a. In the **Number** box, enter the computer (COM) port your TNC is connected to (**1**, **2**, **3**, etc.).

b. In the **Speed** box, enter the baud rate of your TNC serial port (9600 is the default).

c. Select the other operating parameters of the serial port of your TNC (Data Bits, Stop Bits, Parity) by clicking on

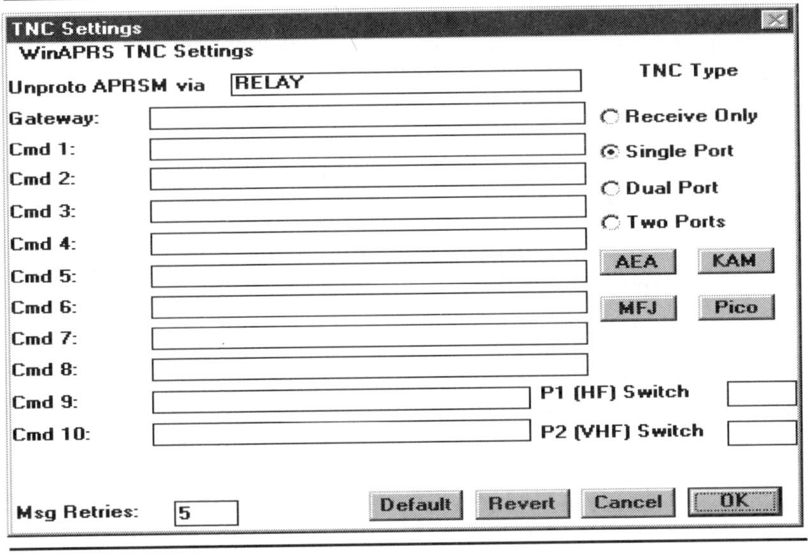

TNC Settings
WinAPRS TNC Settings
Unproto APRSM via RELAY
Gateway:
Cmd 1:
Cmd 2:
Cmd 3:
Cmd 4:
Cmd 5:
Cmd 6:
Cmd 7:
Cmd 8:
Cmd 9:
Cmd 10:
Msg Retries: 5
TNC Type
Receive Only
Single Port
Dual Port
Two Ports
AEA
KAM
MFJ
Pico
P1 (HF) Switch
P2 (VHF) Switch
Default
Revert
Cancel
OK

**Figure 4-11—The WinAPRS TNC Settings window configures WinAPRS for compatibility with your TNC.**

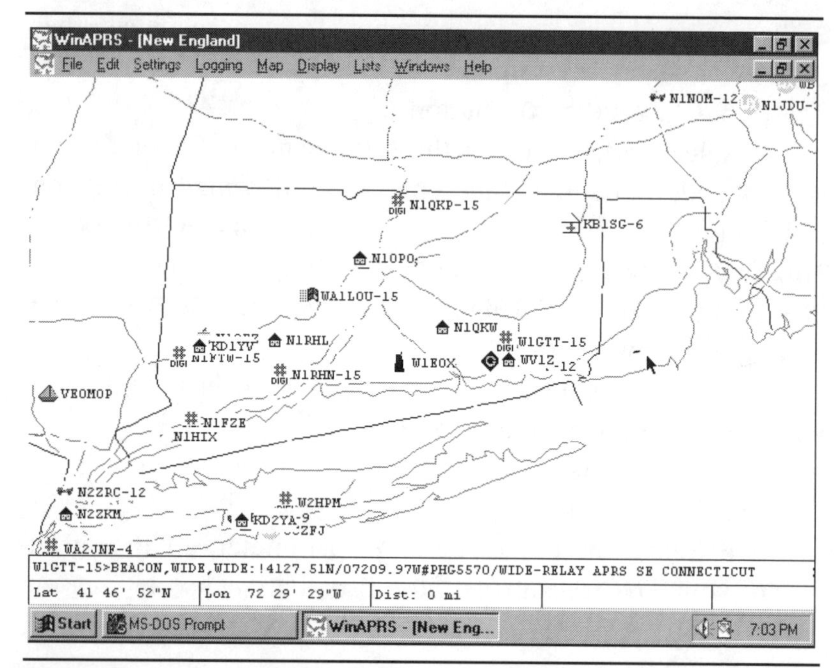


**Figure 4-12—WinAPRS displays what the APRS network looks like on a hot summer night in Southern New England. (Compare it with the Figures 4-2 and 4-7, which display similar maps for the APRSdos and MacAPRS respectively.)**

the appropriate buttons (8 data bits, 1 stop bit, and no parity are the default settings).

d. If another computer serial port is connected to other APRS equipment, then repeat steps a through c for that equipment in the appropriate box (**GPS**, **WX**, or **RDF**) in the **Serial Port Settings** window.

e. Click on the **OK** button.

10. Select **TNC** from the **Settings** menu and enter the following information concerning your TNC in the **TNC Settings** window. (Figure 4-11 illustrates the **WinAPRS TNC Settings** window.)

a. Under **TNC Type**, click on the appropriate buttons for

your TNC: **Receive Only, Single Port, Dual Port, Two Ports, AEA, KAM** (for Kantronics KAM), **MFJ, or Pico** (for PacComm PicoPacket). Depending on your selection(s), WinAPRS loads a set of default commands for your selection(s) in the **Cmd** boxes. These commands are sent to your TNC when WinAPRS initialize your TNC.

b. Click on the **OK** button.

11. Depending on which band(s) you are using, select **Open HF TNC** (dual) or **Open VHF TNC** from the **Settings** menu. Select **Open VHF TNC** for UHF. This causes WinAPRS to initialize your TNC with the parameters you have just set in the previous steps. It also causes WinAPRS to begin transmitting, receiving, and displaying APRS information. Figure 4-12 illustrates the appearance of a WinAPRS map after a few hours of APRS network activity

12. You do not have to save your WinAPRS configuration. Each time you clicked on the **OK** button in the various settings windows, WinAPRS saved your settings automatically. (This function is disabled if your software is not registered. Avoiding reconfiguration each time you start WinAPRS should be plenty of incentive to register the software.)

That completes the initial installation and configuration of WinAPRS. Once you get a feel for your local APRS network, you can fine tune the configuration especially as it relates to the path your APRS packets use and how your APRS station fits into your local APRS network. Later chapters of the book discuss these issues and how you can manage them to the advantage of your station and your local network.

CHAPTER 5

# Getting Around APRS Maps

You have APRS up and running and your APRS map is filling up with icons. You want to join in the fun, but you don't know how. This section of the book tells you how; that is, how to operate your APRS station like an expert, rather than a novice, and have a lot of fun doing it.

You must be able to navigate APRS maps in order to become an expert APRS operator. This chapter describes how to get around each version of APRS and, believe it or not, some of the navigation commands are the same in each version!

## Map Display Basics

There is a slight difference in the way APRSdos and the Mac/Windows versions display maps. In APRSdos, the software always chooses the most detailed map file for a given display range. As you zoom in, if there is another map of finer detail, then it will automatically be loaded. This map layering is necessary due to the limitation of memory in DOS. In Mac/Windows, each map can be almost unlimited in size and be brought up individually in separate windows.

With APRSdos, you display and refresh (redraw) a map by pressing the **Space Bar**. With MacAPRS, you refresh and display a map by entering **Command-L** or selecting **Clear/Redraw** from the **Display** menu; in WinAPRS, you select **Refresh Maps** from **Display** menu. You can center the map on the current position of the cursor by pressing the **Home** key in APRSdos or by selecting **Center View** from the **Display** menu of MacAPRS.

### Magnifying Maps

You magnify (zoom in) a map by pressing the **Page Down** key in all versions of APRS. In MacAPRS, you click on a location then press the **Page Down** key. You may also select **Zoom In 2x** (**Page Down**) or **Zoom In 4x** from the **Display** menu in order to magnify the map two or four times, respectively. In APRSdos holding the **Control Key** while pressing the **Page Up** or **Page Down** key will zoom by a factor of eight.

You zoom out a map by pressing the **Page Up** key in all versions of APRS. In MacAPRS, you may also select **Zoom Out 2x** (**Page Up**) from the **Display** menu.

You may zoom out to the original magnification of the map by pressing the **Home** key in MacAPRS and WinAPRS. Entering **Command-H** in MacAPRS or **D** then **H** in WinAPRS also performs the same function.

You may zoom in any portion of a map that you desire in MacAPRS and WinAPRS. In MacAPRS, press the **Option** key, while clicking on the mouse button and draw a rectangle of the portion of the map you wish to magnify. In WinAPRS, click once with the **Left mouse button** then **Page Down** and double click the **Right mouse button** to select a map with higher resolution.

## Information

In addition to presenting a map, APRS maps display other information usually related to what is happening on the displayed map.

The coordinates of the current position of the cursor on the map appear in the upper left corner of maps in APRSdos, and in the lower left corner of maps in MacAPRS and WinAPRS.

All versions of APRS display the last packet received by your APRS station in the lower portion of the APRS screen.

The bottom of the screen in APRSdos displays the keys to press in order to display screens containing other information. These keys are **A**, **B**, **D**, **H**, **L**, **P**, **V**, **Alt-T**, and **F1** for All beacons, Bulletins, Digipeaters used, Heard log, Latest beacons, Positions, View all packets, Telemetry, and Help, respectively. The bottom of the screen also displays keys to press in order to display command menus. These keys are **X**, **C**, **F**, **I**, **M**, **O**, **W**, and **Alt-S** for Xmit, Controls, Files, Input, Map, Operations, Weather and Set-up, respectively.

To obtain information about a station, in MacAPRS and WinAPRS, double-click on the map icon of the station, and a window telling you all about that station appears. In APRSdos, simply move the cursor to the station and hit **Enter**.

To obtain distance and course information between two points on a map in APRSdos select the first point and hit the **Home** key. Then select the second point and hit **M** (for Maps), **P** (for Plot) and **R** (for range). In MacAPRS and WinAPRS, choose a starting point on the map, click on the mouse button, and drag the cursor to the end point on the map. In MacAPRS, the coordinates of the starting point are displayed in the first pair of **Lat** and **Lon** boxes at the bottom of the screen, the coordinates of the end point are displayed in the second pair of **Lat** and **Lon** boxes, and the distance and course between the two points are displayed in the **Dist:** box at the bottom of the screen. In WinAPRS, the coordinates of the end point are displayed in the **Lat** and **Lon** boxes at the bottom of the screen, and the distance between the two points is displayed in the **Dist:** box at the bottom of the screen.

## After the Fat Lady Sings

When you are finished using APRS, press **Q** in APRSdos, **Command-Q** in MacAPRS, **F** and **X** in WinAPRS. You can also select **Quit** from the **File** menu of MacAPRS or **Exit** from the **File** menu of WinAPRS.

### Map Files

MacAPRS and WinAPRS can handle maps of almost unlimited size. Most of the maps generated are in the order of 50,000 points. Many are 100,000 points and maps that are 700,000 points have been used successfully. Caution: a 700,000 point map will take a few seconds to draw even on a fast computer.

Mac/WinAPRS can handle both map formats at the same time, treating them in the same way. Mac/WinAPRS can handle maps in the APRSdos format that are larger than 3000 points.

Many of the maps used today by all three versions of APRS were generated from United States Geological Survey (USGS) data that is available on CD-ROM and the Internet. This data is very verbose and is *very* complicated. There are several programs that will read this data and allow the generation of maps.

APRSdos reads a map list file to keep track and organize all of the maps that you have. Mac/WinAPRS reads the names of all of the map files in your MAPS directory on startup. Any map from the list can be selected at any time.

Mac/WinAPRS allows you to display the boundaries of all maps. You can select another map by pulling down the **MAPS** menu or bring up the **Map List Window** (not to be confused with the map list file for APRSdos) and double clicking on any map. The map will appear in another window.

A large collection of maps has been put on a CD-ROM by the authors of Mac/WinAPRS. This CD is available for $25 plus $5 for shipping and handling. Contact, Mark Sproul, 698 Magnolia Rd, North Brunswick, NJ 08902.

CHAPTER 6

# Picking a Packet Path

The key to the versatility and flexibility of APRS, especially in an emergency or portable operation, is that it takes advantage of the ability of every TNC to digipeat packets to serve as relays to extend your radio range. The map displays in APRS make it easy to choose the best path for your packets to cover intended area of interest. This makes the path you pick for your packets a very important aspect of APRS. When you got APRS up and running in Chapter 4, the paths were set to their default values. This chapter describes how to fine tune the paths to be compatible with your APRS application and your local APRS network.

The default settings of your packet paths allow you to get up and running without having an intimate knowledge of your local APRS network. Depending on the version of APRS you are using, the default path is typically either RELAY or WIDE.

Wide area APRS digipeaters in your area should have their call sign aliases set to **RELAY** and/or **WIDE** (via the **MYAlias** command). So, when your APRS station sends a packet looking for a path named RELAY or WIDE, the digipeaters in your area with aliases of RELAY and/or WIDE repeat your packet. As a result, you can successfully use APRS digipeaters without having to know their call signs or locations.

This is the key of APRS network operation. Like a novice APRS station, a mobile APRS station passing through unfamiliar territory has no knowledge of the local APRS network. However, if the path of the mobile APRS station is set to **RELAY** or **WIDE** (by means of the **Unproto** command), its packets will be propagated by the digipeaters in the local APRS network.

## APRS Digipeaters

Any fixed APRS station can serve as an APRS digipeater and is encouraged to do so in order to fill in the nooks and crannies of the APRS network. Well-situated, that is, highly elevated, fixed APRS stations are encouraged to serve as wide digipeaters in order to fill in the wide expanses of the APRS network.

The alias of a fixed APRS station serving as a digipeater should be set to **RELAY**. The alias of a wide digipeater should be set to **WIDE** and its second alias (if available) should be set to **RELAY**.

In this way, a wide digipeater can also fill in as a relay digipeater for the nooks and crannies not covered by other relay digipeaters.

A work-around for TNCs with only one alias is to set the call sign to **RELAY** (with the **MYCall** command), set the alias to **WIDE** (with the **MYAlias** command), and let the Beacon function of the TNC take care of the legal identification requirements. The only negative aspect about using this work-around is that your station icon appears on the APRS maps with a label of RELAY or WIDE rather than your call sign. If you do use this work-around, make sure to include your call sign in the beacon (with the **BText** command) and to configure the beacon to be sent every ten minutes or less (set **Beacon Every 599**).

## Fixed APRS Stations

Each non-digipeater fixed APRS station should fine tune its path for compatibility with its local APRS network once it becomes familiar with that network.

Rather than using the generic path of RELAY or WIDE, the path should be set with the call sign of the digipeaters that the fixed station uses to get its packets out into the network. In order to minimize duplication of effort, this is especially critical in areas where the fixed APRS station accesses two or more digipeaters with its RELAY or WIDE path.

The preferable path for a fixed station is to use the call sign of the nearest digipeater followed by one or two WIDEs (**CALLSIGN,WIDE** or **CALLSIGN,WIDE,WIDE**). In this way, the fixed APRS station gets its packets out of its neighborhood in the most efficient way, that is, directly to one digipeater serving its area (by means of the **CALLSIGN** portion of its path). Then that digipeater uses the WIDE portion of the path to propagate the packets of the fixed station out into the APRS network via digipeaters with aliases of WIDE. If you can hit two or more WIDEs from your QTH, you might choose to begin your path with at least one WIDE to get your packets launched simultaneously in more than one direction. If, however, you are only communicating in one direction, then it is best to use specific call signs for each hop.

In areas where there are multiple wides and everyone can hear each other, you should never place three wides in a row. This can lead to a packet being repeated three times for every wide; and each of these is then transmitted three more times and so on. Theoretically, the packet could be digipeated 27 times! This does get the packet sent three times in all directions, but it is extremely inefficient and effectively kills the channel for everyone. In this case, beginning a three hop path with the specific callsign of the first wide digipeater is no different than putting three wides in a row. If you can hit more than one wide directly from your QTH, and you want your packets to go equally in all directions, you should consider beginning your path with WIDE,WIDE. This will launch all of your packets with two hops in all directions while avoiding the triple wide problem. If you want to go three hops or more, then you must use specific callsigns for all digipeaters after the first two wides.

## Mobile APRS Stations

The ideal path for a mobile is always changing, not only because he may be traveling in difficult areas, but also because the topology is always changing. At any instant he may have a direct shot to a wide, while at other times he may be behind a hill, yet close to another station's relay.

The most effective path for a mobile is RELAY,WIDE. This will work whether he is near a wide or only another APRS home station.

## Setting Paths

The following describes how to configure the unprotocol path of your APRS station with each version of APRS.

### APRSdos

To set the unprotocol path with APRSdos:

1. Enter **U**, this will also display a full page help text. After you become familiar with unproto paths, you can use a short-cut under the Operations menu.

2. When prompted, enter the unprotocol path, for example, to set the path to RELAY,WIDE, enter **RELAY,WIDE** with no

space(s) between the words RELAY, WIDE, or the comma between them.

APRSdos allows you to store as many as 12 different paths to use later by simply returning to their two letter abbreviation. Enter **O**, then **D** to access this feature.

## MacAPRS

There are two ways to set the unprotocol path with MacAPRS. The first way is:

1. Select **Unproto APRSM** via (**HF** or **Dual Port**) or **Unproto APRSM** via (**VHF**), whichever is applicable, from the **Settings** menu.

2. Select the unprotocol path you wish to use from the **Unproto APRSM** via sub-menu.

The second way to set the unprotocol path with MacAPRS is:

1. Select **TNC Settings** from the **Settings** menu.

2. Enter the unprotocol path you wish to use in the **Unproto APRSM** via box. Do not use spaces when you enter a path, for example, to enter the path of RELAY,WIDE, type **RELAY,WIDE** with no space(s) between the words RELAY, WIDE, or the comma between them.

3. Click on the **OK** button.

## WinAPRS

To set the unprotocol path with WinAPRS:

1. Select **TNC** from the **Settings** menu.

2. Enter the unprotocol path you wish to use in the **Unproto APRSM** via box. Do not use spaces when you enter a path, for example, to enter the path of RELAY,WIDE, type **RELAY,WIDE** with no space(s) between the words RELAY, WIDE, or the comma between them.

3. Click on the **OK** button.

In areas where there are multiple wides and everyone can hear each other, you should never place three wides in a row. This can lead to a packet being repeated three times for every wide; and each of these is then transmitted three more times and so on. Theoretically, the packet could be digipeated 27 times! This does get the packet sent three times in all directions, but it is extremely inefficient and effectively kills the channel for everyone. In this case, beginning a three hop path with the specific callsign of the first wide digipeater is no different than putting three wides in a row. If you can hit more than one wide directly from your QTH, and you want your packets to go equally in all directions, you should consider beginning your path with WIDE,WIDE. This will launch all of your packets with two hops in all directions while avoiding the triple wide problem. If you want to go three hops or more, then you must use specific callsigns for all digipeaters after the first two wides.

CHAPTER 7

# Tracking

The ability to track moving objects on a map is the primary function (and attraction) of APRS. This function has made APRS an appealing tool for public service communications. The dynamics of tracking public service events require the tracking power of APRS and the ability to replay the track of a moving object just adds to this power.

Tracking requires the moving object to transmit its position as it traverses its route. This may be accomplished automatically via a GPS unit configured to the transmitter in the moving object or manually via operator control. Manual operator control may be performed by an operator inputting position information into a computer running APRS aboard the moving object or remotely by an operator who placed a moving object like a hurricane on an APRS map. In either case, each time a new position is transmitted for a moving object, the icon of that object appears in a new position on everyone's APRS map. (Figure 7-1 illustrates the track of K1TRS-12 along I-84 in central Connecticut using a relatively low resolution map. The eight appearances of the icon on the map indicates the transmission of eight new positions by the APRS equipment aboard K1TRS-12.)

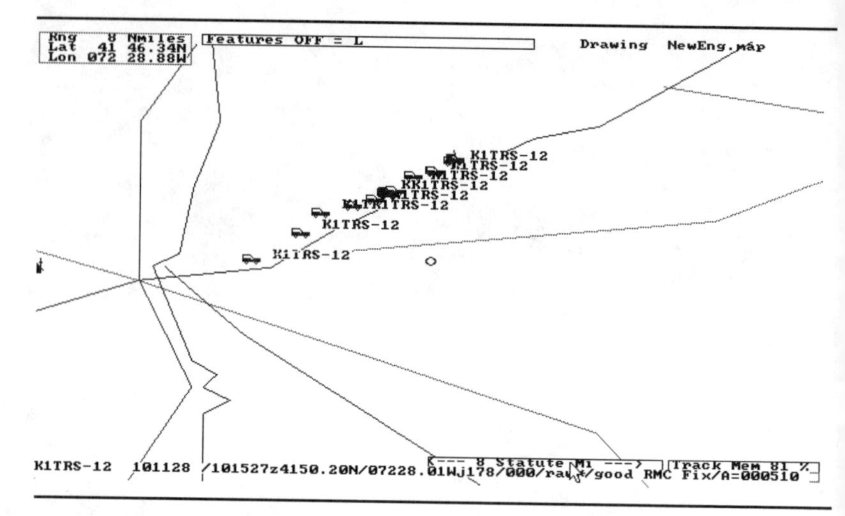


Figure 7-1—APRSdos tracks K1TRS-12 along I-84 in central Connecticut.

Replaying the track of a moving object is performed differently by APRSdos and Mac/WinAPRS. For starters, to replay the track of one object in APRSdos, you must select the object beforehand; otherwise, APRS replays all of the activity on the channel not just the object you are interested in replaying. With MacAPRS and WinAPRS, you can select one moving object at any time to replay the entire track of that object only.

Another difference is how the three versions of APRS display a replay of a track. With APRSdos, a replay of a tracked object duplicates the original display of that object. That is, the icon of the moving object is displayed at each position along its route wherever it transmitted a new position. (With APRSdos, a replay of the track illustrated in Figure 7-1 would appear exactly like Figure 7-1.) With MacAPRS and WinAPRS, the software draws a solid line along the route of the tracked object from the beginning to the end of its route. (Figure 7-2 illustrates the original track of K1TRS-12 with MacAPRS and Figure 7-3 illustrates the replay of that same track with MacAPRS. WinAPRS performs in a similar fashion.)

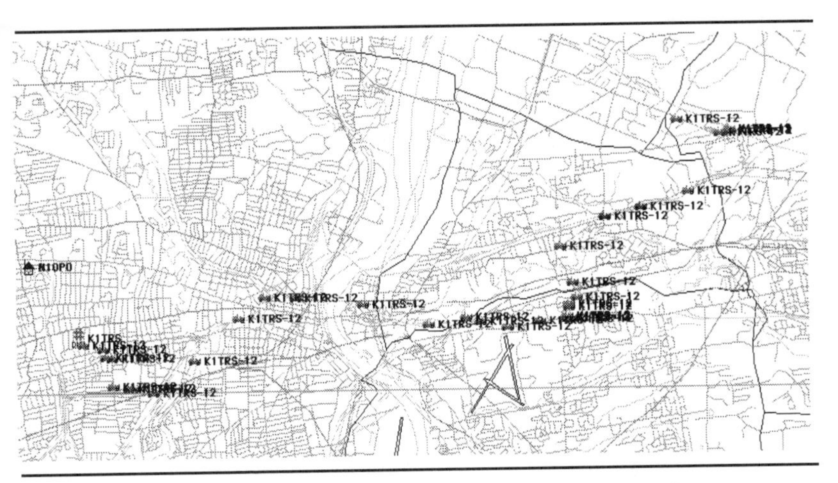


**Figure 7-2 MacAPRS tracks K1TRS-12 along I-84 in central Connecticut.**

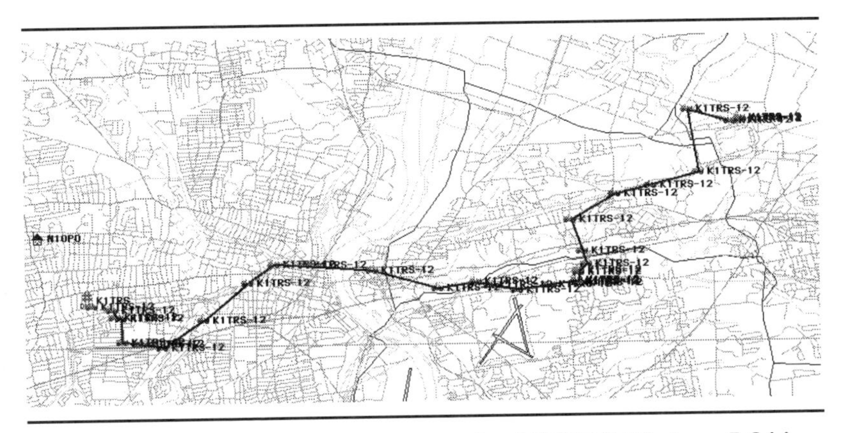


**Figure 7-3—MacAPRS replays the track of K1TRS-12 along I-84 in central Connecticut.**

## Tracking and Instant Replays

The following describes how to track and replay tracked stations with each version of APRS. In general, all stations on frequency will be tracked and their track histories stored in all versions of APRS.

## APRSdos

To force APRSdos to not only track a station, but to also keep the map display centered on a moving station, you may call up the Positions page with the **P** command.

1. Then move the cursor to the call sign of the station you wish to track.

2. Enter **T** (for Track).

To replay the track of any station whose track may still be in on-line memory:

1. Enter **O** (for Operations), then **R** (for Replay).

2. Enter the call sign of the station whose track you wish to replay.

If the track history has already been stored to the Track History file, then you must replay from the file. Enter **F** (for Files) and **R** (for Replay).

## MacAPRS

To replay the track of a station with MacAPRS:

1. Choose the station whose track you wish to replay.

2. Click on the most recent icon (the last position received) of that station on the map.

3. Select **Replay Selected Station** from the **Display** menu or enter **Command-R**.

## WinAPRS

To replay the track of a station with WinAPRS:

1. Choose the station whose track you wish to replay.

2. Click on the most recent icon (the last position received) of that station on the map.

3. Select **Replay Track** from the **Display** menu or enter **D** then **R**.

CHAPTER 8

# Adding Objects to Maps

Besides your APRS station, you can add other things to the APRS map and they will appear on all the APRS maps in your network. For example, you can display the path of a hurricane, the lead runner in a marathon, the lead vehicle in a parade, or a mobile communications control center in an emergency or natural disaster scenario.

Let us use the hurricane example. Hurricane Hiram is coming up the coast. You obtain its coordinates, speed, and course from the National Weather Service, the Weather Channel, or some other reliable source. With this information in hand, you access the add object function of APRS, and input the name, coordinates, speed, and course of the hurricane. You also select an appropriate icon for the APRS map display (enter the @ in order to display the hurricane icon). (Figure 8-1 illustrates an object, Hurricane Hiram, that an APRS user placed on a map.)

As you receive updates concerning the position, speed, and course of Hurricane Hiram, you access APRS and enter the updated information in order to adjust the icon of the hurricane

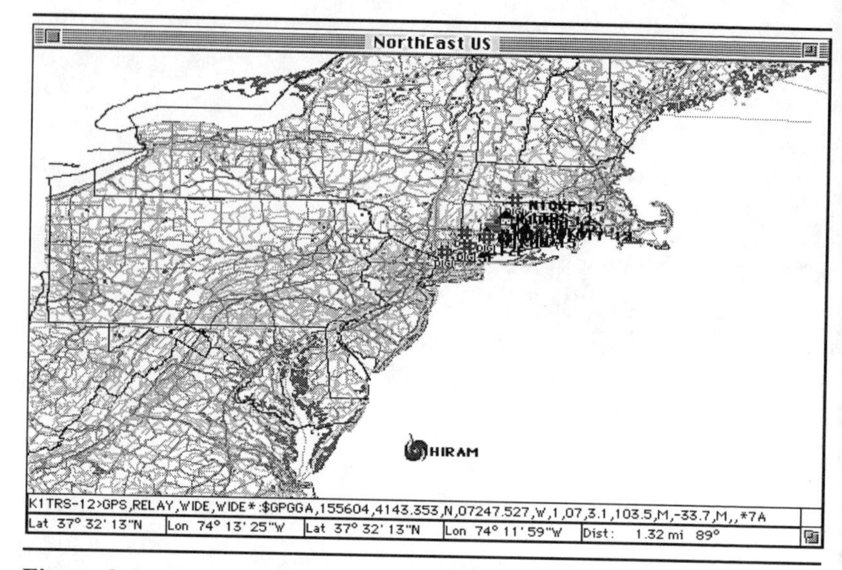


**Figure 8-1—The icon of Hurricane Hiram moving up the East Coast is under the control of an APRS station operator.**

on the APRS map. And, when the hurricane is over, you access APRS to remove the hurricane icon from the APRS map.

## Adding Objects

The following describes how to add or delete an object on an APRS map with each version of APRS. It also describes how to change the position of an object on an APRS map.

### APRSdos

To add an object to an APRS map with APRSdos:

1. Enter **I** (for Input), then **A** (for Add).

2. When prompted, enter the requested information concerning the object. (The current position of your cursor on the map is the latitude and longitude displayed in the prompt.)

To change the position of an object on a map with APRSdos:

1.Move the cursor to the icon of the object on the APRS map.

2. Press **Enter.**

3. Move the cursor to the new location of the object on the APRS map.

4. Press **Insert.**

To delete an object from an APRS map with APRSdos either select it with the cursor on the map or from the Positions Table.

1. Move the cursor to the object you wish to delete.

2. Press **Enter**.

3. Enter **D** (for Delete).

4. Enter **Y** to delete the object from the maps of the other APRS stations on frequency. Answering Yes sends out a kill-object packet, a No deletes it only from your map.

## MacAPRS

To add an object to an APRS map with MacAPRS:

1. Select **Edit/Add Station/Objects...** from the **Edit** menu or enter **Command-E.**

2. Enter and select the parameters of the object you wish to add in the **Add Object** or **Station** window. (The latitude and longitude displayed in the **Latitude:** and **Longitude:** boxes is the current position of your cursor on the map.)

3. Click on the **OK** button.

To change the position of an object on an APRS map with MacAPRS:

1. Click on the icon for the object on the APRS map.

2. Select **Edit/Add Station/Objects...** from the Edit menu or enter **Command-E**.

3. Enter and select the parameters of the object you wish to change in the **Add Object** or **Station** window.

4. Click on the **OK** button.

To delete an object from an APRS map with MacAPRS:

1. Select **Clear Stations and Messages**, from the **Edit** menu.

2. Select **Clear/Redraw** from the Display menu or enter **Command-L**.

## WinAPRS

To add an object to an APRS map with WinAPRS:

1. Select **Edit/Add Station/Objects...** from the Edit menu.

2. Enter and select the parameters of the object you wish to add in the **Add Object** or **Station** window. (The latitude and longitude displayed in the **Latitude:** and **Longitude:** boxes is the current position of your cursor on the map.)

3. Click on the **OK** button.

To change the position of an object on an APRS map with WinAPRS:

1. Click on the icon for the object on the APRS map.

2. Select **Edit/Add Station/Objects...** from the **Edit** menu.

3. Enter and select the parameters of the object you wish to change in the **Add Object** or **Station** window.

4. Click on the **OK** button.

To delete an object from an APRS map with WinAPRS, select **Clear Stations and Msgs** from the **Edit** menu.

CHAPTER 9

# Keyboard Communications

Sometimes an APRS map itself is not enough and you have to send a text message to another station to pass information concerning activity being displayed on the map. Or you may have a need to pass information to all the stations in the APRS network.

The authors of APRS foresaw this need and as a result, the software supports communications in real-time. The software accomplishes this by permitting you to send one-line messages to any active station in the APRS network or by sending multiple-line bulletins to all the stations in the network.

## Sending Messages

The following describes how to send a message to another station with each version of APRS.

### APRSdos

To send a message to another station with APRSdos:

1. Enter **S** (for Send).

2. At the **To:** prompt, enter the call sign of the station that is the intended recipient of the message.

3. At the **Entr MsgText:** prompt, enter the contents of the message.

### MacAPRS

To send a message to another station with MacAPRS:

1. Select **New Message...** from the **Windows** menu or enter **Command-M**.

2. In the **To:** box, enter the call sign of the station that is the intended recipient of the message.

3. In the **Msg:** box, enter the contents of the message.

4. Click on the **OK** button.

### WinAPRS

To send a message to another station with WinAPRS:

1. Select **New Message...** from the **Lists** menu.

2. In the **To:** box, enter the call sign of the station that is the intended recipient of the message.

3. In the **Msg:** box, enter the contents of the message.

4. Click on the **Send** button or enter **S**.

## Reading Messages

The following describes how to read a message from another station with each version of APRS.

### APRSdos

To read a message from another station with APRSdos, enter **R** (Read) and a window appears that lists the message sent by your station and addressed to your station. (Figure 9-1 illustrates the **Message** window.)

### MacAPRS

To read a message from another station with MacAPRS,

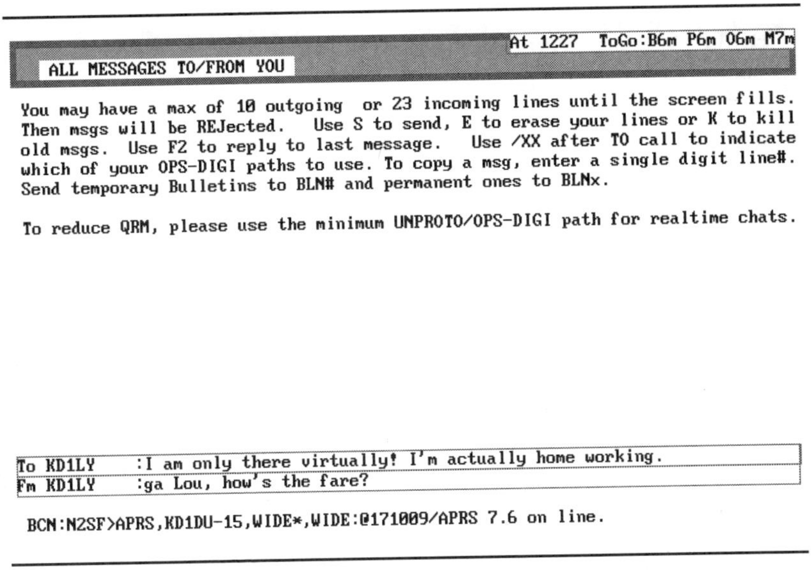

```
                                                      At 1227  ToGo:B6m P6m O6m M7m
  ALL MESSAGES TO/FROM YOU

You may have a max of 10 outgoing  or 23 incoming lines until the screen fills.
Then msgs will be REJected.  Use S to send, E to erase your lines or K to kill
old msgs.  Use F2 to reply to last message.  Use /XX after TO call to indicate
which of your OPS-DIGI paths to use. To copy a msg, enter a single digit line#.
Send temporary Bulletins to BLN# and permanent ones to BLNx.

To reduce QRM, please use the minimum UNPROTO/OPS-DIGI path for realtime chats.




To KD1LY     :I am only there virtually! I'm actually home working.
Fm KD1LY     :ga Lou, how's the fare?

 BCN:N2SF>APRS,KD1DU-15,WIDE*,WIDE:@171009/APRS 7.6 on line.
```

**Figure 9-1—The message window in APRSdos lists messages sent by your station and addressed to your station.**

select **Message List** from the **Windows** menu or enter **Command-4** and the **Message List** window appears containing all the messages sent and received by your station.

The messages are color-coded to differentiate messages addressed to or from you from those addressed to other stations. Color-coding also differentiates messages sent by your station that have and have not been received by their intended recipient. (Figure 9-2 illustrates the **Message List** window.)

## WinAPRS

To read a message from another station with WinAPRS, select **Message List** from the **Lists** menu and the **Message List** window appears containing all the messages sent and received by your station.

The messages are color-coded to differentiate messages addressed to or from you from those addressed to other stations.

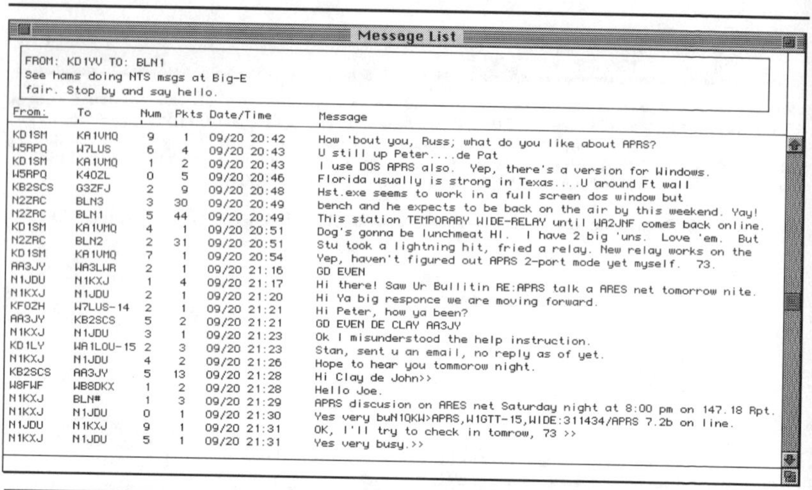

Message List

FROM: KD1YV TO: BLN1
See hams doing NTS msgs at Big-E
fair. Stop by and say hello.

| From: | To | Num | Pkts | Date/Time | Message |
|---|---|---|---|---|---|
| KD1SM | KA1VMQ | 9 | 1 | 09/20 20:42 | How 'bout you, Russ; what do you like about APRS? |
| W5RPQ | W7LUS | 6 | 4 | 09/20 20:43 | U still up Peter....de Pat |
| KD1SM | KA1VMQ | 1 | 2 | 09/20 20:43 | I use DOS APRS also. Yep, there's a version for Windows. |
| W5RPQ | K4OZL | 0 | 5 | 09/20 20:46 | Florida usually is strong in Texas....U around Ft wall |
| KB2SCS | G3ZFJ | 2 | 9 | 09/20 20:48 | Hst.exe seems to work in a full screen dos window but |
| N2ZRC | BLN3 | 3 | 30 | 09/20 20:49 | bench and he expects to be back on the air by this weekend. Yay! |
| N2ZRC | BLN1 | 5 | 44 | 09/20 20:49 | This station TEMPORARY WIDE-RELAY until WA2JNF comes back online. |
| KD1SM | KA1VMQ | 4 | 1 | 09/20 20:51 | Dog's gonna be lunchmeat HI. I have 2 big 'uns. Love 'em. But |
| N2ZRC | BLN2 | 2 | 31 | 09/20 20:51 | Stu took a lightning hit, fried a relay. New relay works on the |
| KD1SM | KA1VMQ | 7 | 1 | 09/20 20:54 | Yep, haven't figured out APRS 2-port mode yet myself. 73. |
| AA3JY | WA3LWR | 2 | 1 | 09/20 21:16 | GD EVEN |
| N1JDU | N1KXJ | 1 | 4 | 09/20 21:17 | Hi there! Saw Ur Bullitin RE:APRS talk a ARES net tomorrow nite. |
| N1KXJ | N1JDU | 2 | 1 | 09/20 21:20 | Hi Ya big responce we are moving forward. |
| KF0ZH | W7LUS-14 | 2 | 1 | 09/20 21:21 | Hi Peter, how ya been? |
| AA3JY | KB2SCS | 5 | 2 | 09/20 21:21 | GD EVEN DE CLAY AA3JY |
| N1KXJ | N1JDU | 3 | 1 | 09/20 21:23 | Ok I misunderstood the help instruction. |
| KD1LY | WA1LOU-15 | 2 | 3 | 09/20 21:23 | Stan, sent u an email, no reply as of yet. |
| N1KXJ | N1JDU | 4 | 2 | 09/20 21:26 | Hope to hear you tommorow night. |
| KB2SCS | AA3JY | 5 | 13 | 09/20 21:28 | Hi Clay de John>> |
| W8FWF | WB8DKX | 1 | 2 | 09/20 21:28 | Hello Joe. |
| N1KXJ | BLN# | 1 | 3 | 09/20 21:29 | APRS discusion on ARES net Saturday night at 8:00 pm on 147.18 Rpt. |
| N1KXJ | N1JDU | 0 | 1 | 09/20 21:30 | Yes very buN1QKW>APRS,W1GTT-15,WIDE:311434/APRS 7.2b on line. |
| N1JDU | N1KXJ | 9 | 1 | 09/20 21:31 | OK, I'll try to check in tomrow, 73 >> |
| N1KXJ | N1JDU | 5 | 1 | 09/20 21:31 | Yes very busy.>> |

**Figure 9-2—The Message List window in MacAPRS lists all the messages sent and received by your station.**

Color-coding also differentiates messages sent by your station that have and have not been received by their intended recipient. (Figure 9-2 illustrates the MacAPRS **Message List** window, which is very similar to the **Message List** window of WinAPRS.)

By default the WinAPRS **Message List** displays all the messages and bulletins sent and received by your station, however, by clicking the **My Messages Only** button in the **Message List** window, the window only displays those messages sent by your station and addressed to your station. Clicking the **All** messages button causes the **Message List** to return to its default, that is, displaying all messages and bulletins.

## Sending Bulletins

The following describes how to send a bulletin to other stations with each version of APRS.

## APRSdos

To send a bulletin to other stations with APRSdos use the same technique for other messages, except choose the **To** address to be BLN#.

1. Enter **S** (Send).
2. At the **To:** prompt, enter **BLN1**.
3. At the **Entr MsgText:** prompt, enter the contents of one line of the bulletin.
4. If your bulletin is one line in length, then you are finished. If your bulletin is longer, enter **S** again.
5. The **To:** prompt defaults to **BLN2**. Press **Enter**.
6. At the **Entr MsgText:** prompt, enter the contents of the second line of the bulletin.
7. Stop if you are finished entering the bulletin or continue entering **S** until you finish entering each line of a multiple line bulletin (up to a maximum of 9 lines, **BLN1** to **BLN9**).

## MacAPRS

To send a bulletin to other stations with MacAPRS:

1. Select **New Message...** from the **Windows** menu or enter **Command-M**.
2. Click on the **Bulletin** button.
3. In the **Msg:** box, enter the contents of the bulletin.
4. Click on the **OK** button.

## WinAPRS

To send a bulletin to other stations with WinAPRS:

1. Select **New Message...** from the **Lists** menu.
2. Click on the **Bulletin** button.
3. In the **Msg:** box, enter the contents of the bulletin.
4. Click on the **Send** button or enter **S**.

# Reading Bulletins

The following describes how to read bulletins with each version of APRS.

## APRSdos

To read bulletins with APRSdos, enter **B** and a window appears that lists the bulletins received to your station. (Figure 9-3 illustrates the bulletin window.)

## MacAPRS

To read bulletins with MacAPRS, select **Message List** from the **Windows** menu or enter **Command-4** and the **Message List** window appears containing all the bulletins sent and received by your station. The bulletins are color-coded to differentiate them from messages sent and received by your station. (Figure 9-2 illustrates the **Message List** window.)

## WinAPRS

To read bulletins with WinAPRS, select **Message List** from the **Lists** menu and the **Message List** window appears containing all the bulletins sent and received by your station.

```
BULLETINS OF GENERAL INTEREST            At 1225  ToGo:B8m P8m O8m M2m
                                          alt-E to ERASE Bltns

KD1YV> BLN1 :See hams doing NTS msgs at Big-E fair. Stop by and say hello.

N1JDU-3>BLN1:N1SWK has bad Lat/Lon info in pos report. Only 2 digits after
N1JDU-3>BLN2:decimal are allowed. Lat is ok, but Lon has 3. Will not show
N1JDU-3>BLN3:up on any APRS map this way. Have uploaded him as object >>

N2ZRC> BLN1 :This station TEMPORARY WIDE-RELAY until WA2JNF comes back online.
N2ZRC> BLN2 :Stu took a lightning hit, fried a relay. New relay works on the
N2ZRC> BLN3 :bench and he expects to be back on the air by this weekend. Yay!

W5RPQ> BLN2 :Propagation is the pits in Texas last 18 hours....de
```

**Figure 9-3—The bulletin window in APRSdos lists bulletins received by your station.**

The bulletins are color-coded to differentiate them from messages sent and received by your station. (Figure 9-2 illustrates the MacAPRS **Message List** window, which is very similar to the **Message List** window of WinAPRS.)

By default, the WinAPRS **Message List** displays all the messages and bulletins sent and received by your station. However, by clicking the **Bulletins Only** button in the **Message List** window, the window only displays bulletins. Clicking the **All Messages** button causes the **Message List** to return to its default, that is, displaying all messages and bulletins.

CHAPTER 10

# Displaying Other Data

There is a wealth of information that you may get from APRS in addition to what the book has already described. Although this data usually appears in a list, some of it appears graphically. The following descriptions highlight some of the more important data that you can access with APRS.

## Station Data

All three versions of APRS allow you to obtain information about the stations that are active on your APRS network.

APRSdos provide the following information concerning each station: call sign, day and time of reception, day and time of entry, latitude, longitude, course, speed, and contents of identification string, if any. (Figure 10-1 illustrates the **Positions** display of APRSdos.)

MacAPRS and WinAPRS lists the stations received by your station in their order of receipt (the oldest first) and provide the following information concerning each station: map icon, call sign, station type (if any), number of packets received, time of first receipt, and contents of identification string (if any). (Figure 10-2 illustrates the **Station Lists** window of MacAPRS, which is very similar to the **Station Lists** window of WinAPRS.)

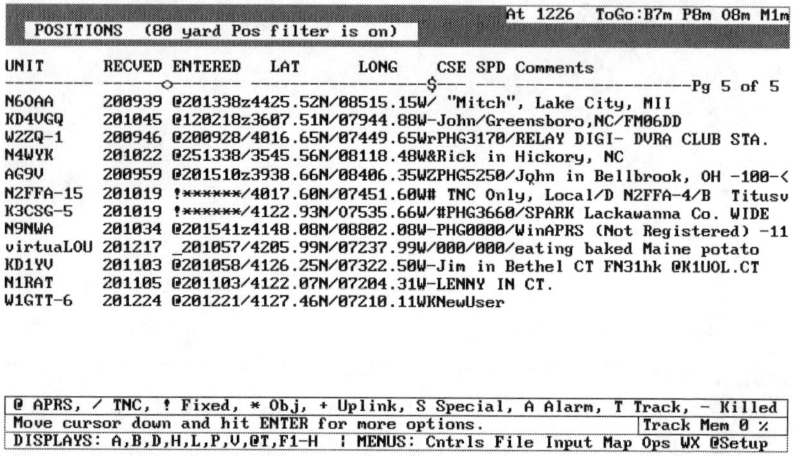

```
                                                    At 1226   ToGo:B7m P8m O8m M1m
 POSITIONS  (80 yard Pos filter is on)
UNIT       RECVED ENTERED    LAT       LONG     CSE SPD Comments
---------- ------o------- -----------------$--- --- ------------------Pg 5 of 5
N6OAA      200939 @201338z4425.52N/08515.15W/ "Mitch", Lake City, MII
KD4VGQ     201045 @120218z3607.51N/07944.88W-John/Greensboro,NC/FM06DD
W2ZQ-1     200946 @200928/4016.65N/07449.65WrPHG3170/RELAY DIGI- DVRA CLUB STA.
N4WYK      201022 @251338/3545.56N/08118.48W&Rick in Hickory, NC
AG9V       200959 @201510z3938.66N/08406.35WZPHG5250/John in Bellbrook, OH -100-<
N2FFA-15   201019 !******/4017.60N/07451.60W# TNC Only, Local/D N2FFA-4/B  Titusv
K3CSG-5    201019 !******/4122.93N/07535.66W/#PHG3660/SPARK Lackawanna Co. WIDE
N9NWA      201034 @201541z4148.08N/08802.08W-PHG0000/WinAPRS (Not Registered) -11
virtuaLOU  201217 _201057/4205.99N/07237.99W/000/000/eating baked Maine potato
KD1YV      201103 @201058/4126.25N/07322.50W-Jim in Bethel CT FN31hk @K1UOL.CT
N1RAT      201105 @201103/4122.07N/07204.31W-LENNY IN CT.
W1GTT-6    201224 @201221/4127.46N/07210.11WKNewUser

@ APRS, / TNC, ! Fixed, * Obj, + Uplink, S Special, A Alarm, T Track, - Killed
Move cursor down and hit ENTER for more options.              Track Mem 0 %
DISPLAYS: A,B,D,H,L,P,V,@T,F1-H  ! MENUS: Cntrls File Input Map Ops WX @Setup
```

**Figure 10-1—The Positions window of APRSdos lists the APRS stations received by your station.**

Station List

Total Stations = 62

| Type | Call | CATOF | Pkts | Time | ID-String |
|---|---|---|---|---|---|
| | WA1LOU-15 | M F | 149 | 22:34 | @210234z4137.86N/07256.73WMPHG9581/The Wolcott Bicentennial |
| | N1RHL | – | 71 | 22:26 | |
| DIGI | W1GTT-15 | # | 64 | 22:34 | W1GTT-15/R WIDE/D W1GTT-14/B RELAY/N |
| GPS | N1QKP-9 | > T | 61 | 20:15 | |
| | N1NOM | y | 14 | 22:27 | N1NOM/R RELAY/D N1NOM-1/B |
| | WB1F | _ | 79 | 22:27 | WB1F/R WB1F-3/G WB1F-1/B |
| DIGI | N2ZRC | # | 164 | 22:35 | N2ZRC/R WIDE/D N2ZRC-4/B |
| DIGI | N2SF | # | 25 | 22:16 | |
| | N1JDU-3 | _ | 11 | 22:10 | N1JDU-3/R RELAY/D N1JDU-1/B WATER/N |
| | KD1YV | – | 115 | 20:21 | |
| | KB2SCS | – | 52 | 21:47 | |
| | K2MEB | | 6 | 19:47 | |
| | K1TRS | – | 58 | 22:27 | K1TRS/R RELAY/D K1TRS-1/B K1TRS-7/N |
| DIGI | N1FTW-15 | # | 48 | 22:28 | |

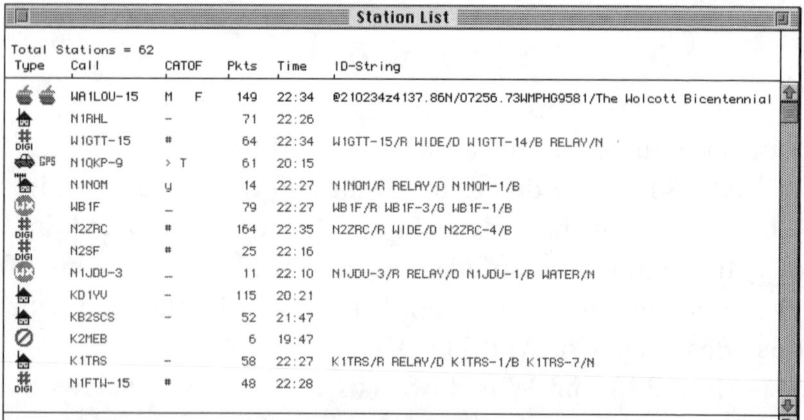

**Figure 10-2—The Station Lists window of MacAPRS delineates the APRS stations received by your station.**

The following describes how to obtain station data with each version of APRS:

- APRSdos: Enter **P**.
- MacAPRS: Select **Station List** from the **Windows** menu or enter **Command-1**.
- WinAPRS: Select **Station List** from the **Lists** menu.

## Digipeater List

APRSdos allows you to obtain a list of the digipeaters used by each APRS station received by your station. The list includes the call sign and digipeater path of each station. An asterisk (*) next to the station call sign indicates that you received at least one of the packets directly from that station, not via a digipeater. An asterisk next to a digipeater indicates that you received the last packet from that station via the digipeater. Enter **D** to display the **Digipeater List**. (Figure 10-3 illustrates the Digipeater List of APRSdos.)

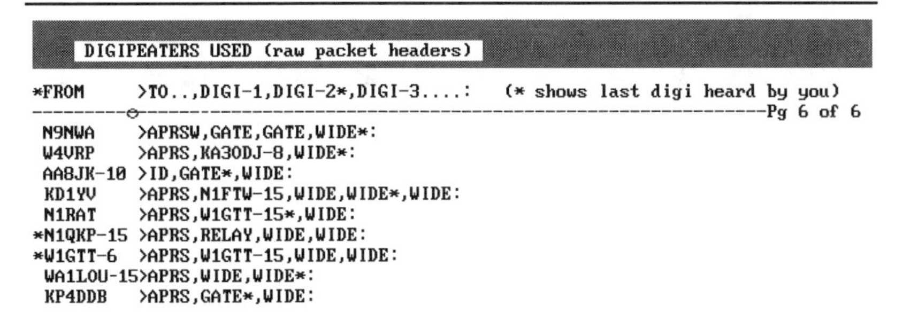

```
DIGIPEATERS USED (raw packet headers)
*FROM      >TO..,DIGI-1,DIGI-2*,DIGI-3....:   (* shows last digi heard by you)
----------------------------------------------------------------------Pg 6 of 6
 N9NWA     >APRSW,GATE,GATE,WIDE*:
 W4VRP     >APRS,KA3ODJ-8,WIDE*:
 AA8JK-10 >ID,GATE*,WIDE:
 KD1YV     >APRS,N1FTW-15,WIDE,WIDE*,WIDE:
 N1RAT     >APRS,W1GTT-15*,WIDE:
*N1QKP-15 >APRS,RELAY,WIDE,WIDE:
*W1GTT-6   >APRS,W1GTT-15,WIDE,WIDE:
 WA1LOU-15>APRS,WIDE,WIDE*:
 KP4DDB    >APRS,GATE*,WIDE:

Move cursor down and hit ENTER for more options. !VIA WIDE,WIDE
DISPLAYS: A,B,D,H,L,P,V,@T,F1-H  ! MENUS: Cntrls File Input Map Ops WX @Setup
```

**Figure 10-3—The Digipeater List of APRSdos lists the digipeaters used by the APRS stations received at your station.**

MacAPRS and WinAPRS do not have a Digipeater List function. If you double-click the icon of a station on an APRS map, however, the software displays the digipeater information concerning that station.

## Heard List

Each version of APRS has a function that lists the number of packets received per hour from each station over the previous 24-hour period. APRSdos presents this data in a tabular format, while MacAPRS and WinAPRS present this data graphically. (Figures 10-4 and 10-5 illustrate the APRSdos and MacAPRS versions of the display, respectively. The WinAPRS version of this display is very similar to the MacAPRS version.)

The following describes how to obtain the Heard List with each version of APRS:

- APRSdos: Enter **H**.

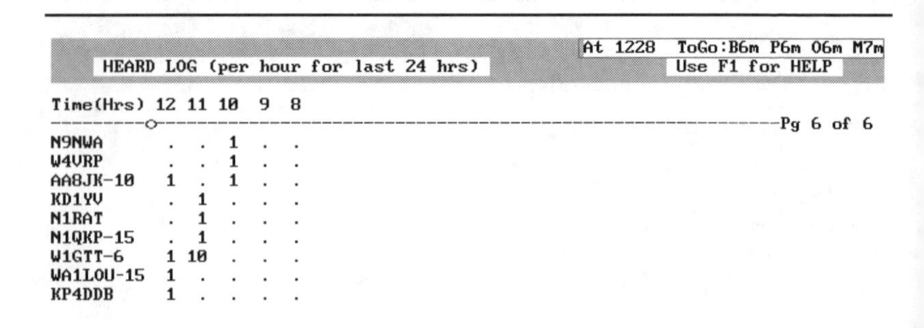


**Figure 10-4—The Heard Log of APRSdos lists the number of packets received each hour in a tabular format.**

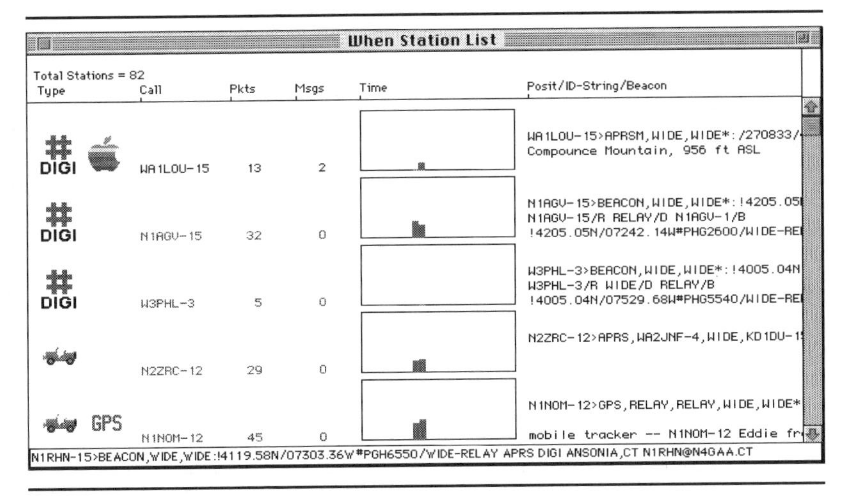


**Figure 10-5—The When Station List of MacAPRS lists the number of packets received each hour graphically.**

- MacAPRS: Select **When List** from the **Windows** menu or enter **Command-2.**
- WinAPRS: Select **When Heard** from the **Lists** menu.

## Weather Data

All versions of APRS have a Weather List function that lists the weather stations received by your station in their order of receipt (the oldest first). The Weather List includes the following information concerning each station: map icon, call sign, time of last packet received, air temperature, rain fall measurements, atmospheric pressure, wind speed, wind gusts, wind direction, number of alarms generated by the station, and the Weather List stations distance from your station. (Figure 10-6 illustrates the Weather List window of MacAPRS, which is very similar to the Weather List window of WinAPRS.)

The following describes how to obtain the Weather List with MacAPRS and WinAPRS:

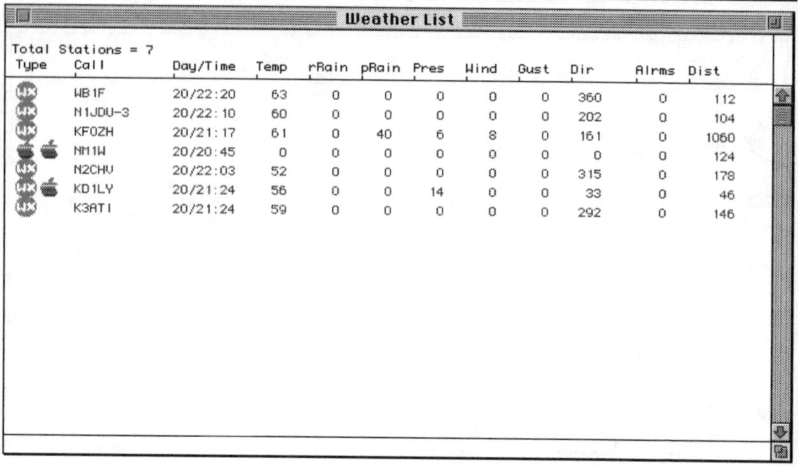

Weather List

Total Stations = 7

| Type | Call | Day/Time | Temp | rRain | pRain | Pres | Wind | Gust | Dir | Alrms | Dist |
|---|---|---|---|---|---|---|---|---|---|---|---|
| WX | WB1F | 20/22:20 | 63 | 0 | 0 | 0 | 0 | 0 | 360 | 0 | 112 |
| WX | N1JDU-3 | 20/22:10 | 60 | 0 | 0 | 0 | 0 | 0 | 202 | 0 | 104 |
| WX | KF0ZH | 20/21:17 | 61 | 0 | 40 | 6 | 8 | 0 | 161 | 0 | 1060 |
|  | NM1W | 20/20:45 | 0 | 0 | 0 | 0 | 0 | 0 | 0 | 0 | 124 |
| WX | N2CHV | 20/22:03 | 52 | 0 | 0 | 0 | 0 | 0 | 315 | 0 | 178 |
| WX | KD1LY | 20/21:24 | 56 | 0 | 0 | 14 | 0 | 0 | 33 | 0 | 46 |
| WX | K3ATI | 20/21:24 | 59 | 0 | 0 | 0 | 0 | 0 | 292 | 0 | 146 |

**Figure 10-6—The Weather List of MacAPRS delineates the weather data received from the APRS weather stations.**

• MacAPRS: Select **Weather List** from the **Windows** menu or enter **Command-3**.

• WinAPRS: Select **Weather List** from the **Lists** menu.

The MacAPRS and WinAPRS versions also have a Weather Display function that graphically represents the output of the weather station, if any, that is configured with your APRS station.

The following describes how to obtain the Weather Display with MacAPRS and WinAPRS:

• MacAPRS: Select **Weather Display** from the **Windows** menu or enter **Command-8**.

• WinAPRS: Select **Weather Display** from the **Lists** menu.

APRSdos does not have a Weather List function per se, although it does have a number of other options for obtaining weather data from the weather stations on the APRS network.

For APRSdos, press the **J** (Just), **W** (Weather) keys. If you are currently on the map display, all non-weather related icons will disappear leaving only weather related features on the map. If you are on the **Positions** display, the **Just** weather command will present a tabular display of weather reports.

By entering **W**, then **D**, then **R**, APRSdos replaces the call signs of the weather stations on the APRS map with the time, atmospheric pressure and rainfall measurements. By entering **W**, then **D**, then **T**, the call signs are replaced with the temperature and rainfall measurements. And by entering **W**, then **D**, then **W**, the call signs are replaced with the time, wind speed, and rainfall measurements. The line extending from the icon of a weather station indicates the direction of the wind.

## View Packets

All three versions of APRS permit you to obtain a list of the packets received by your station. APRSdos displays the last 12 packets received, whereas, MacAPRS and WinAPRS displays all the packets received by your station. (Figures 10-7 and 10-8 respectively illustrate the view packets displays of APRSdos and MacAPRS. The WinAPRS display is very similar to the MacAPRS display.)

The following describes how to view packets with each version of APRS:

- APRSdos: Enter **V**.
- MacAPRS: Select **History** from the **Windows** menu or enter **Command-5**.
- WinAPRS: Select **History** from the **Lists** menu.

## Station Lists

APRSdos maintains a Latest Status List which lists the latest status packet received from each station. MacAPRS and WinAPRS have a Flagged Station List function that lists the flagged stations received by your station in their order of receipt (the oldest first). The Flagged Station List includes the

```
                                                     At 1227  ToGo:B6m P6m O6m M15

*** LAST 12 packets in VIEW BUFFER:
N2SF>APRS,KD1DU-15*,WIDE,WIDE:N2ZRC    :Why does KD1DU use 3 wides??{2

N2ZRC>APRS,KD1DU-15*,WIDE,WIDE:N2SF     :ack2

N2ZRC>APRS,KD1DU-15,WIDE*,WIDE:N2SF     :ack2

N2SF>APRS,KD1DU-15,WIDE*,WIDE:N2ZRC    :Why can I digipt via kd1du-15, but not

N2ZRC>APRS,KD1DU-15,WIDE,WIDE*:N2SF     :ack2

N2ZRC>APRS,KD1DU-15*,WIDE,WIDE:N2SF     :ack3

N2ZRC>APRS,KD1DU-15,WIDE*,WIDE:N2SF     :ack3

VIEW MODE!  Colors show results of APRS parsing.  CANCEL WITH ANY OTHER SCREEN.
```

**Figure 10-7—The View Packets list of APRSdos displays the last 12 packets received.**

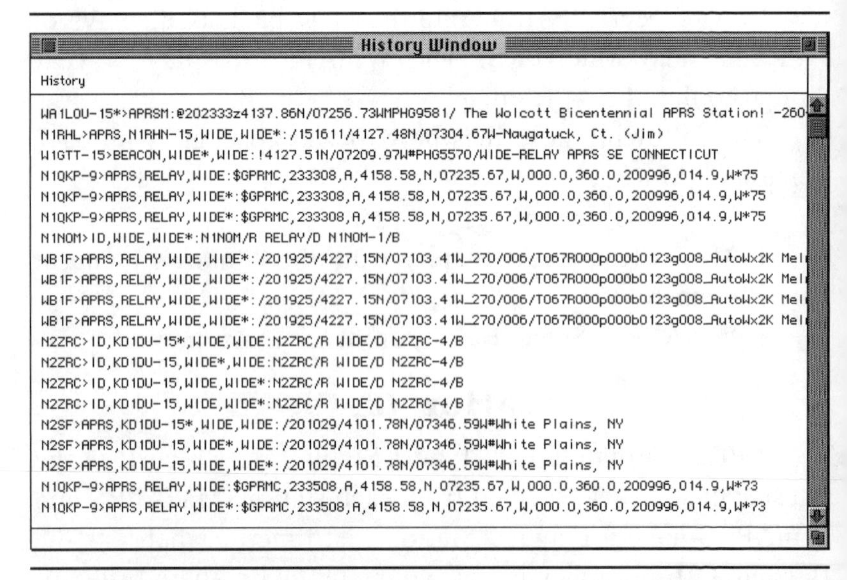


**Figure 10-8—The History Window of MacAPRS lists all the packets received by your station.**

following information concerning each station: map icon, call sign, time of first receipt, number of packets received, distance from your station, version of MacAPRS and/or WinAPRS being used by the station, computer type, and contents of identification string (if any). (Figure 10-9 illustrates the Flagged Station List of MacAPRS, which is very similar to the WinAPRS Flagged Station List.)

The following describes how to obtain the Station Lists with each version:

- APRSdos: Enter **L** (Latest).
- MacAPRS: Select **Flagged Station List** from the **Windows** menu.
- WinAPRS: Select **Flagged Station List** from the **Lists** menu.

By the way, to flag stations in MacAPRS, select **MacAPRS Settings...** from the **Settings** menu and click on the **Auto Flag**

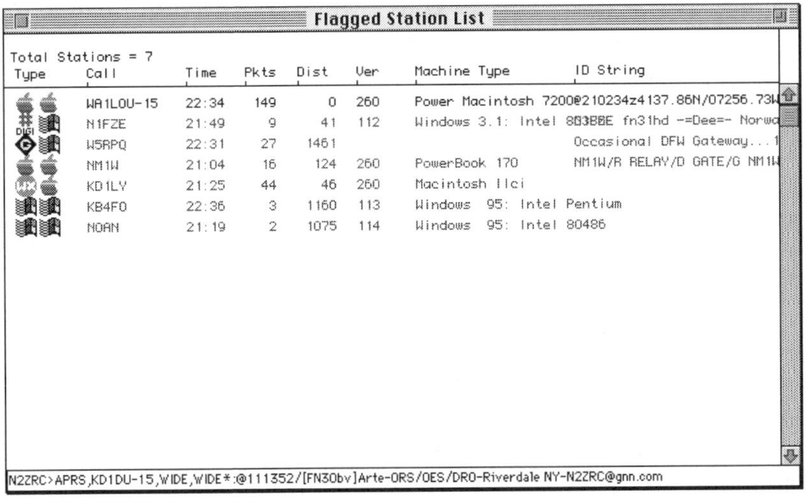

**Flagged Station List**

Total Stations = 7

| Type | Call | Time | Pkts | Dist | Ver | Machine Type | ID String |
|---|---|---|---|---|---|---|---|
| | WA1LOU-15 | 22:34 | 149 | 0 | 260 | Power Macintosh 7200 | @210234z4137.86N/07256.73W |
| DIGI | N1FZE | 21:49 | 9 | 41 | 112 | Windows 3.1: Intel | 803B0E fn31hd -=Dee=- Norwa |
| G | W5RPQ | 22:31 | 27 | 1461 | | | Occasional DFW Gateway...1 |
| | NM1W | 21:04 | 16 | 124 | 260 | PowerBook 170 | NM1W/R RELAY/D GATE/G NM1W |
| | KD1LY | 21:25 | 44 | 46 | 260 | Macintosh IIci | |
| | KB4FO | 22:36 | 3 | 1160 | 113 | Windows 95: Intel Pentium | |
| | N0AN | 21:19 | 2 | 1075 | 114 | Windows 95: Intel 80486 | |

N2ZRC>APRS,KD1DU-15,WIDE,WIDE*:@111352/[FN30bv]Arte-ORS/OES/DRO-Riverdale NY-N2ZRC@gnn.com

**Figure 10-9—The Flagged Station List of MacAPRS delineates the flagged stations received by your station.**

**Macs** and/or **Auto Flag Windows** buttons, then click on the **OK** button.

To flag stations in WinAPRS, select **APRS** from the **Settings** menu and click on the **Auto Flag Macs** and/or **Auto Flag Windows** buttons, then click on the **OK** button. You can also flag any station by selecting it in **Station List Window** and then hit **F**.

## Tracked Station List

All versions have a list of the positions of all stations being tracked. In APRSdos, it is called the Positions List. MacAPRS and WinAPRS have a Tracked Station List function that lists the tracked stations received by your station in their order of receipt (the oldest first). The Tracked Station List includes the following information concerning each station: map icon, call sign, time of last packet received, number of packets received, track, course, speed, altitude, distance traveled, distance from your station, and contents of identification string, if any. (Figure 10-10 illustrates the Tracked Station List of MacAPRS, which is very similar to the WinAPRS Tracked Station List.)

The following describes how to obtain the Tracked Station List with the various versions.

- APRSdos: Enter **P** (Positions).
- MacAPRS: Select **Tracked Station List** from the **Windows** menu.
- WinAPRS: Select **Track List** from the **Lists** menu.

## Map List

All versions permit you to view the various map that are available to the system. In APRSdos, the display is graphical, showing the outline of all the maps. In Mac and Win versions, the information is in a list.

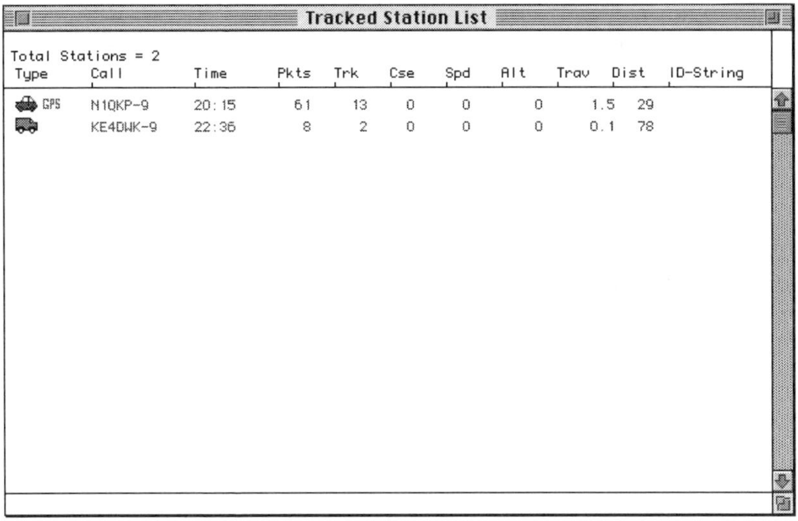

Tracked Station List

Total Stations = 2

| Type | Call | Time | Pkts | Trk | Cse | Spd | Alt | Trav | Dist | ID-String |
|---|---|---|---|---|---|---|---|---|---|---|
| GPS | N1QKP-9 | 20:15 | 61 | 13 | 0 | 0 | 0 | 1.5 | 29 | |
| | KE4DWK-9 | 22:36 | 8 | 2 | 0 | 0 | 0 | 0.1 | 78 | |

**Figure 10-10—The Tracked Station List of MacAPRS delineates the tracked stations received by your station.**

The following describes how to obtain the Map List:

- APRSdos: Enter **M** (Map), **P** (Plot), then **B** (Border). Then use function keys **F3** and **F4** to display more or less borders.
- MacAPRS: Select **Map List** from the **Windows** menu.
- WinAPRS: Select **Map List** from the **Lists** menu.

## Icon List

All versions of APRS allow you to view all the icons that may be used to represent stations and objects on the map. APRSdos displays all the icons in their ASCII order. MacAPRS and WinAPRS display the following information concerning each icon: the icon itself, the key on your computer keyboard that you press to select the icon, and the name of the icon. (Figure 10-11 illustrates all the map icons available in APRS, their keyboard equivalents, and names.)

**Figure 10-11—The APRS map icons.**

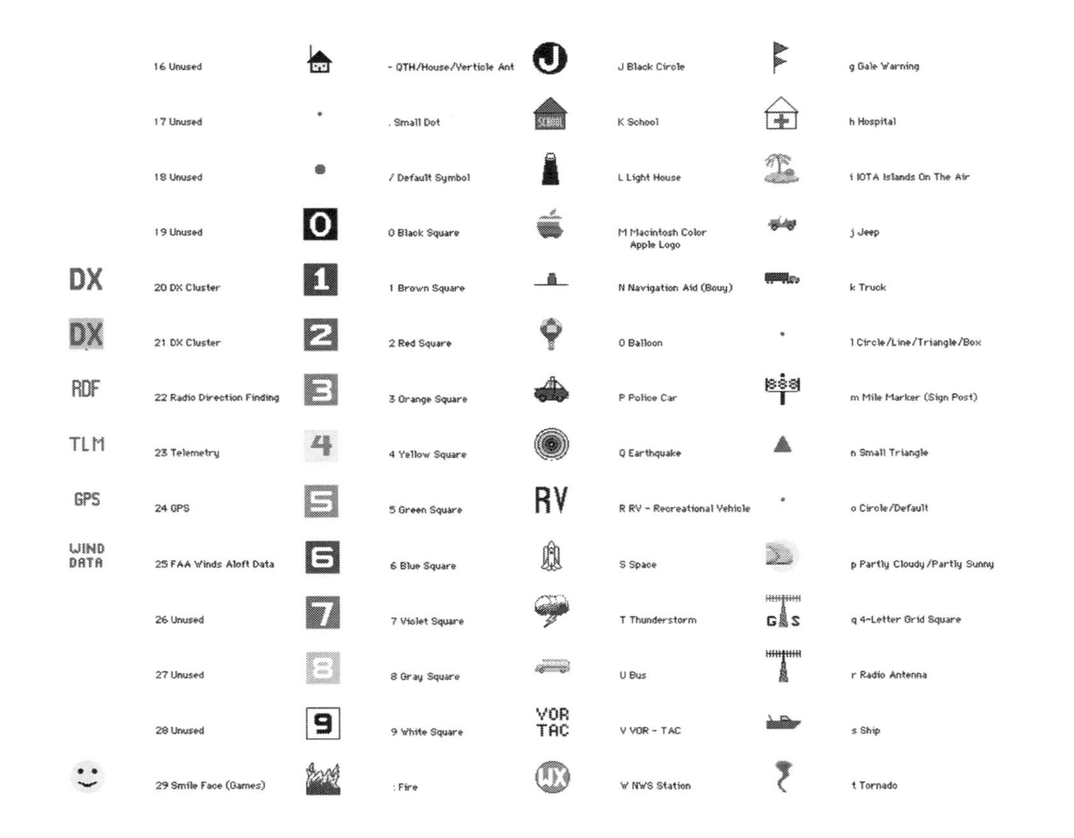
DX
DX
RDF
TLM
GPS
WIND DATA
16 Unused
- QTH/House/Verticle Ant
J Black Circle
g Gale Warning
17 Unused
. Small Dot
K School
h Hospital
18 Unused
/ Default Symbol
L Light House
i IOTA Islands On The Air
19 Unused
0 Black Square
M Macintosh Color Apple Logo
j Jeep
20 DX Cluster
1 Brown Square
N Navigation Aid (Bouy)
k Truck
21 DX Cluster
2 Red Square
O Balloon
l Circle/Line/Triangle/Box
22 Radio Direction Finding
3 Orange Square
P Police Car
m Mile Marker (Sign Post)
23 Telemetry
4 Yellow Square
Q Earthquake
n Small Triangle
24 GPS
5 Green Square
R RV - Recreational Vehicle
o Circle/Default
25 FAA Winds Aloft Data
6 Blue Square
S Space
p Partly Cloudy/Partly Sunny
26 Unused
7 Violet Square
T Thunderstorm
q 4-Letter Grid Square
27 Unused
8 Gray Square
U Bus
r Radio Antenna
28 Unused
9 White Square
V VOR - TAC
s Ship
29 Smile Face (Games)
: Fire
W NWS Station
t Tornado

The following describes how to obtain the Icon List with each version of APRS:

- APRSdos: Enter **F1** (help), then **S** (for Symbol).
- MacAPRS: Select **Icon Type** from the **Windows** menu.
- WinAPRS: Select **Symbol List** from the **Lists** menu.

CHAPTER 11

# Direction Finding

Direction finding is the process of locating the source of an unknown radio signal. Direction finding is essential when that unknown radio signal is causing interference, intentional or unintentional, to other radio stations.

Traditionally, direction finding was an acquired art demanding a lot of practice and patience, as well as some specialized equipment. APRS has lessened this burden and permits more stations to participate in direction finding. Even stations that lack directional antennas can participate in the hunt just like their beam-equipped ham radio brethren.

## Omni-Directional Direction Finding

In the past, there was one requirement that no station could ignore in order to participate in direction finding: the need for a directional antenna and the ability to move that antenna to obtain a bearing on the unknown radio signal that was the object of the hunt. Now, APRSdos permits groups and individual stations equipped with omni-directional antennas to participate in the hunt. (At this time, MacAPRS and WinAPRS do not support omni-directional direction finding.)

## Group Omni-Directional Direction Finding

The following describes how to use APRSdos for omni-directional direction finding with a group of stations.

1. Each APRS station participating in the hunt should monitor the channel on which the unknown radio signal is transmitting.

2. Each APRS station should enter the signal strength of the unknown radio signal into APRSdos. If a station does not detect any signal, this information is also valuable and should be entered into APRSdos. To enter the signal strength of the unknown radio signal:

a. Enter **I** (for Input), then enter **D** (for DF).

b. Enter **0**. Next, enter the relative signal strength (1 to 9) of the unknown radio signal or enter 0 if you detect no signal. Use the following table for entering the relative signal strength (RSS):

| RSS | Description |
|---|---|
| 0 | No signal detected |
| 1 | Barely detectable signal |
| 2 | Detectable signal, but extremely weak and unreadable |
| 3 | Weak and barely readable signal |
| 4 | Noisy, but readable signal |
| 5 | Readable signal, but with some noise |
| 6 | Good signal, but with detectable noise |
| 7 | Very good signal with very little detectable noise |
| 8 | Strong signal with no detectable noise |
| 9 | Very strong signal (with no detectable noise) |

3. Each APRS station (or one or two designated stations) should check the local voice repeaters seeking omni-directional signal reports from any stations wishing to assist in the hunt.

4. Each voice station that assists in the hunt must be

entered into APRS. In addition to the signal strength reported by each voice station, you also need its location, height above average terrain (HAAT), antenna gain, and the compass direction (in degrees) that their antenna favors, if any. To enter this information:

a. Enter **I** (for Input), then **A** (for AddObj).

b. When prompted, enter the requested information concerning the voice station. (The current position of your cursor on the map is the latitude and longitude displayed in the Latitude and Longitude prompts.) Be sure to enter **D** (for DF) at the **Symbols** prompt, **0** at the **DF Bearing** prompt, and the signal strength of the unknown station as reported by the voice station at the **Relative Signal Strength** prompt. If no signal is detected by the voice station, enter **0** at the **Relative Signal Strength** prompt.

5. Enter **M** (for Maps), then **P** (for Plots), and **D** (for DF). APRS plots the relative signal strength data on the map in a manner that helps to pinpoint the source of the unknown radio signal.

First, APRS plots the largest circles around those stations that gave weakest signal reports. The weaker the signal report, the larger the circle because if the signal is weak, then it likely originates from a farther distance than if the signal is strong. The farther distance translates to a larger coverage circle.

After plotting the largest coverage circles, APRS plots continuously smaller circles representing continuously stronger signal reports. After plotting the smallest coverage circles, which represent the strongest signal reports, it plots gray-colored coverage circles that represent the coverage areas of stations that gave no signal reports, that is, the stations that could not hear any signal from the unknown station.

To interpret this display:

a. Eliminate the areas covered by the gray coverage

circles. Nothing was heard in the gray coverage circles, so the unknown radio signal cannot be located within the grayed areas.

b. Locate the greatest concentration of non-gray circle intersections. The unknown radio signal is likely to be emanating from this area of the map.

Figure 11-1 illustrates a simple example of a group APRS direction finding display. The coverage circles labeled A and B are gray and represent the areas where no signal was received. You can eliminate these gray areas as the possible source of the unknown radio signal.

Coverage circle C is the largest and represents the weakest signal report. Coverage circle E is the smallest and represents the strongest signal report. Coverage circle D falls somewhere

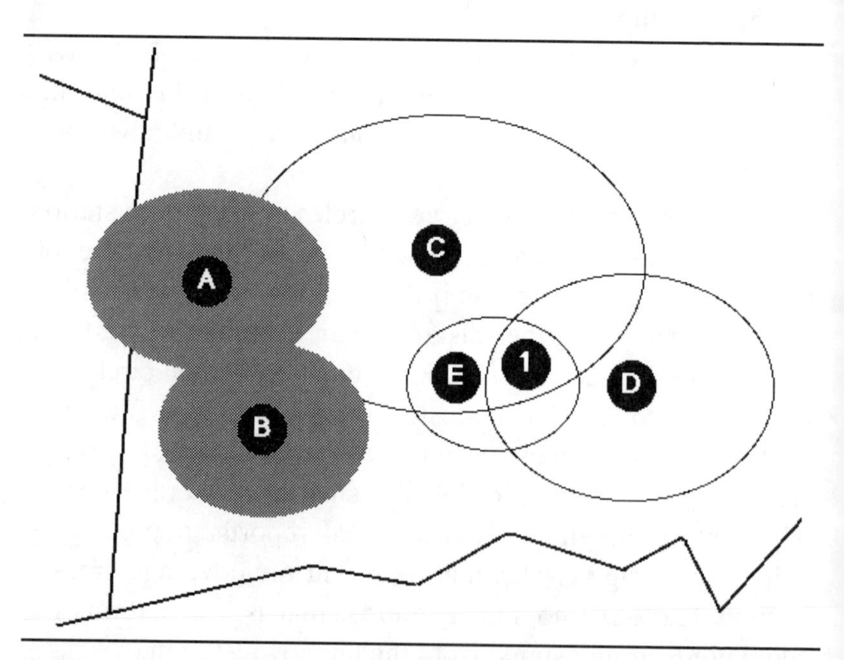


**Figure 11-1—A simplified example showing how APRS displays the results of a group of stations using omni-directional antennas for direction finding.**

in between C and E in size and signal strength. The area labeled 1 represents the greatest concentration of non-gray circle intersections. Area 1 is likely to be the source of the unknown radio signal.

## Solo Omni-Directional Direction Finding

Using APRSdos omni-directional direction finding on an individual basis requires a different technique than that used for omni-directional direction finding with a group. Instead of using signal strength and bearing information, the solo omni-directional direction finding station must find the points where the unknown radio signal fades in or out. By plotting these fade points on an APRS map, you are able to locate the source of the unknown radio signal at the center of the plotted fade points.

You must find and plot a minimum of three fade points for successful solo omni-directional direction finding. To discover these points, monitor the unknown radio signal while traveling through the general area of its source. When the radio signal fades in or out, you have found a fade point and should enter it into APRS. Fading in occurs as you travel into the coverage area of the unknown radio signal, whereas fading out occurs as you travel out of the coverage area.

To narrow your search area, you may attenuate your receiver or tighten its squelch. As a result, the fade points occur closer to each other. Narrowing your search field is a good strategy to use after you have plotted a wide area search field with no attenuation and/or the squelch wide open.

To use APRSdos for solo omni-directional direction finding:

1. Press the **F5** (Function 5) key whenever you discover a fade point.

2. At the **New Pass Configuration** prompt, enter **Y** (for Yes) for the first fade point entry and enter **N** (for No) for subsequent

fade point entries. Only enter **Y** again if you change your radio configuration, e.g., you use a different antenna, attenuate your receiver, tighten the squelch, etc.

3. After entering three or more fade points, enter **M** (for Maps), then **P** (for Plots), and **F** (for FadeDF) to display the APRSdos calculation of the location of the unknown radio signal. Figure 11-2 illustrates the result of a solo APRS direction finding expedition using three fade points.

In this example, WA1LOU traveled south and began hearing the unknown radio signal at the fade point labeled (LOU)G1. Continuing to travel south, the unknown radio signal disappeared at fade point (LOU)G2. WA1LOU turned right and traveling west-northwest, reacquired the unknown radio signal at fade point (LOU)G3. The intersection of the three dotted bearing lines indicates the calculated position of the unknown radio signal based on the three fade points.

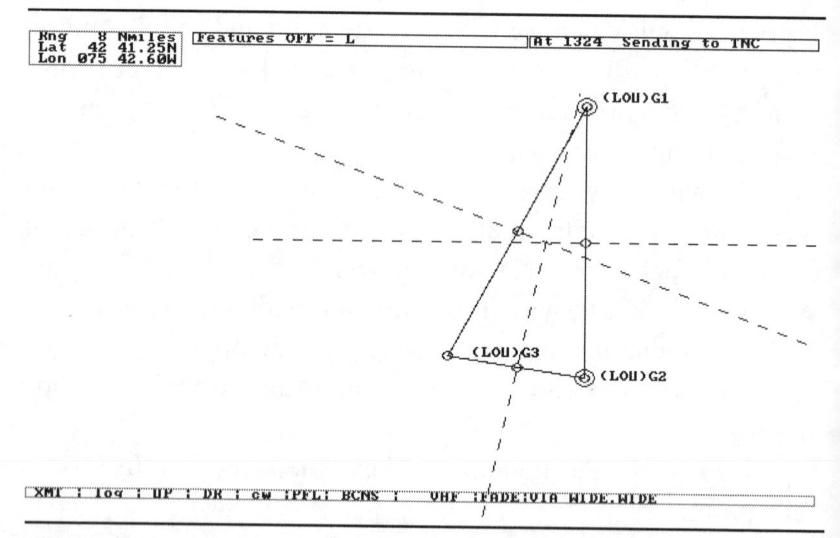


**Figure 11-2—A simple example of a solo APRS direction finding display using three fade points.**

For a more accurate calculation of the location of the unknown radio signal source, you need more than three fade point entries. Notice how the calculated position shifts when WA1LOU enters a fourth fade point at (LOU)G4, as illustrated in Figure 11-3. The calculated location of the unknown radio signal is at the intersection of the two solid lines plotted between fade points G1-G3 and G2-G4.

## Directional Direction Finding

APRS supports traditional direction finding, that is, direction finding using beam antennas or specialized direction finding equipment such as a Doppler measuring device like the DFjr, which is a compact, Doppler-based direction finding system specifically designed for APRS operation. The DFjr was developed by Joe Agrelo, N2OOC, and is available from Agrelo Engineering, PO Box 231, Pattersonville, NY 12137,

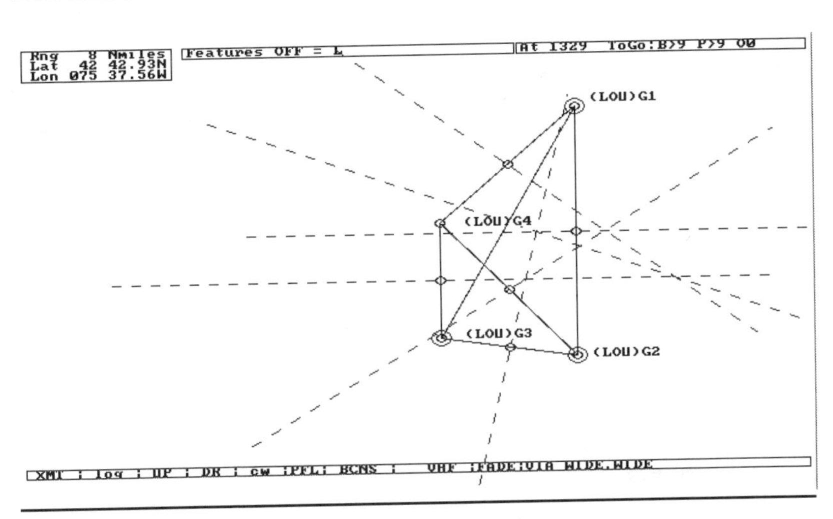


**Figure 11-3—Entering additional fade points results in more accurate solo APRS direction finding.**

phone 518-864-7551, fax 518-864-7553, e-mail **Jagrelo @cris.com**. With a device like the DFjr and a GPS unit interfaced to your APRS station, you can enjoy automatically generated real time displays of direction finding vectors with all three versions of APRS.

Using beam antennas for direction finding requires more work. You must manually enter the beam headings of the unknown radio signal into APRS. (Only APRSdos supports manual entry of beam headings.)

To enter a beam heading into APRSdos:

1. Enter **I** (for Inputs), then **D** (for DF).
2. At the **DF Bearing** prompt, enter the beam heading (in degrees) of the unknown radio signal (use 360 for 0 degrees north).
3. At the **Enter Quality** prompt, enter a value between 1 and 8 (8 being the best) for the quality of the unknown radio signal.

After entering the information requested by APRS, the program draws a yellow line on the map representing the beam heading you entered. A solid line indicates a good quality signal. Dotted lines indicate lesser quality signals. Other APRS stations that are hunting for the source of the unknown radio signal should also enter their beam headings and APRS displays them on the map, too.

Non-APRS stations may also join in the hunt. To add a non-APRS station beam heading report to the map:

1. Enter **I** (for Input), then **A** (for AddObj).
2. When prompted, enter the requested information concerning the non-APRS station. (The current position of your cursor on the map is the latitude and longitude displayed in the Latitude and Longitude prompts.) Be sure to enter **D** (for DF) at the **Symbols** prompt, the reported beam heading at the **DF Bearing** prompt (use 360 for 0 degrees north), and the quality of the unknown radio signal at the **Enter Quality** prompt.

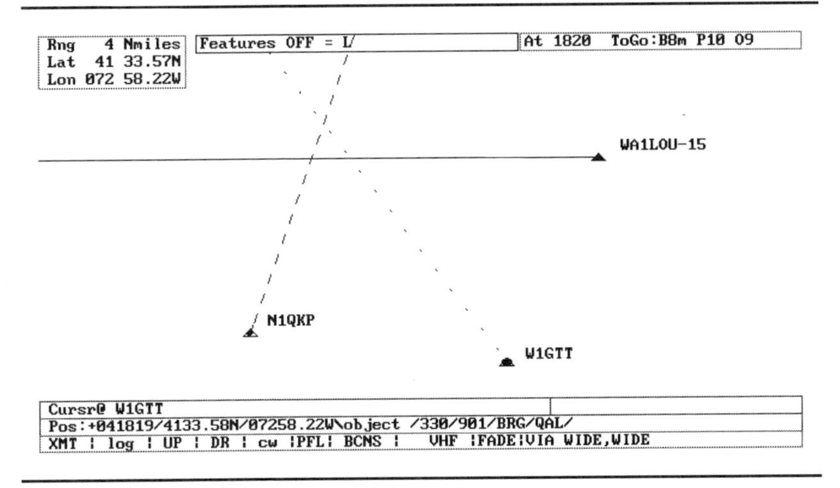


**Figure 11-4—APRSdos displays the manually entered beam headings of three stations attempting to find the source of an unknown radio signal.**

Figure 11-4 illustrates the result of the manual entry of beam headings. In this example, APRS station WA1LOU-15 entered a beam heading of 270 degrees with a signal quality of 8. Non-APRS stations N1QKP and W1GTT respectively reported beam headings of 15 and 330 degrees and signal quality estimates of 4 and 1. WA1LOU entered their reports and Figure 11-4 is the result. The source of the unknown radio signal likely resides near the center of the triangle formed by the three beam headings.

CHAPTER 12

# Monitoring Telemetry

APRS is able to receive and display telemetry from diverse moving objects such as balloons aloft and animals in the wild. The telemetry can be diverse, too. For example, it may include such information as the current altitude of a balloon or the current body temperature of an animal. GPS can also be used to provide position information of these moving objects.

The key to monitoring telemetry with APRS is the Micro Interface Module (MIM), which is a complete telemetry TNC in one integrated circuit. MIM has five analog and eight digital inputs, which may be sampled at a user-selectable time period. Each sample is output in a standard AX.25 packet. Telemetry sensors on the MIM input, a transmitter on the MIM output, and a battery are all you need to complete the package. GPS can be used optionally as an input.

Carl Wick, N3MIM, developed the MIM and he worked with Will Clement, N3XLM, to massage MIM for APRS. MIMs are available from Clement Engineering, Inc., PO Box 1086, Severna Park, MD 21146, phone 410-268-6736, fax 410-268-4612, e-mail **wiclement@aol.com**.

# Initializing a Telemetry Scenario

MIM telemetry transmissions consist of packets containing a string of data that represents each sampling of its inputs. Any station can receive these packets, but the data contained in these packets is meaningless.

In order to make this data meaningful, a designated APRS station must set the stage for the telemetry scenario. This is accomplished by sending four messages over the APRS network. The first message defines the telemetry labels, the second message defines the telemetry units, the third message defines the telemetry equations, and the fourth message defines the digital bit definitions and the project name.

Stations wishing to receive meaningful telemetry, must receive the four messages. If they do, their APRS software extracts information from these messages in order to display received telemetry in a meaningful manner. Figure 12-1 shows the APRSdos Telemetry window displaying the following

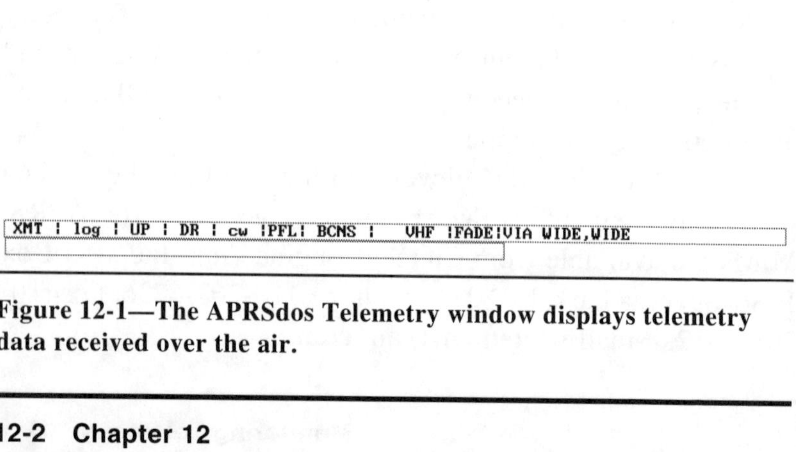

```
 APRS TELEMETRY FOR HORZEPA'S ZEPPELIN      At 1141   ToGo:B7m P28      M1m

SER TIME Alt        Temp    Press Batt
         Ft         Deg     In    V
--- ---- ---------  ------- ----- -----
101 1228    11000        80    28  12.0
102 1229    14000        82    28  12.0

XMT | log | UP | DR | cw |PFL| BCNS |   VHF |FADE|VIA WIDE,WIDE
```

**Figure 12-1—The APRSdos Telemetry window displays telemetry data received over the air.**

information concerning a balloon launch: altitude, temperature, pressure, and battery measurements.

## APRSdos

To initialize a telemetry scenario with APRSdos:

1. Enter **S**.
2. At the **To**: prompt, enter the call sign of the MIM.
3. At the **Entr MsgText**: prompt, enter the telemetry labels.

The format for the telemetry labels is PARM. P1,P2,P3,P4,P5,B1,B2,B3,B4,B5,B6,B7, where P1 through P5 and B1 through B7 are the parameter names (for example, PARM.Alt,Temp,Press,Batt). The maximum length of each parameter is 9 characters for P1, 8 characters for P2, 6 each for P3 through P5, 5 each for B1 through B3, and 4 each for B4 through B7.

4. Enter **S** again.
5. At the **To**: prompt, enter the call sign of the MIM.
6. At the **Entr MsgText**: prompt, enter the telemetry units.

The format for the telemetry units is UNIT.C1,C2, C3,C4,C5,D1,D2,D3,D4,D5,D6,D7, where C1 through C5 are the units for analog ports and D1 through D7 are the labels for the bits (for example, UNIT.Ft,Deg,In,V). The maximum length of each unit is 9 characters for C1, 8 characters for C2, 6 each for C3 through C5, 5 each for D1 through D3, and 4 each for D4 through D7.

7. Enter **S** again.
8. At the **To**: prompt, enter the call sign of the MIM.
9. At the **Entr MsgText**: prompt, enter the telemetry equations.

The format for the telemetry equations is EQNS.E1,F1,G1,E2,F2,G2,E3,F3,G3,E4,F4,G4,E5,F5,G5 where E1 through E5, F1 through F5, and G1 through G5 are the coefficients of a quadratic equation for each of the five analog channels (for example, EQNS.0.53,0,0,0). The quadratic equation is $H = EJ^2 + FJ + G$ where H is the final value and J is the value transmitted by the MIM.

10. Enter **S** again.

11. At the **To**: prompt, enter the call sign of the MIM.

12. At the **Entr MsgText**: prompt, enter the digital bit definitions and the project name.

The format for the digital bit definitions and the project name is BITS.KKKKKKKK,L where KKKKKKKK indicates whether the on-state of each of the digital inputs is represented by a 0 or 1 and where L is the name of the project up to 23 characters in length (for example, BITS.10110000,Horzepa's Zeppelin).

13. Stop when you are finished entering the fourth message.

## MacAPRS

To initialize a telemetry scenario with MacAPRS:

1. Select **New Message...** from the **Windows** menu or enter **Command-M**.

2. In the **To**: box, enter the call sign of the MIM.

3. In the **Msg**: box, enter the telemetry labels.

The format for the telemetry labels is PARM. P1,P2,P3,P4,P5,B1,B2,B3,B4,B5,B6,B7, where P1 through P5 and B1 through B7 are the parameter names (for example, PARM.Alt,Temp,Press,Batt). The maximum length of each parameter is 9 characters for P1, 8 characters for P2, 6 each for P3 through P5, 5 each for B1 through B3, and 4 each for B4 through B7.

4. Click on the **OK** button.

5. Select **New Message...** from the **Windows** menu or enter **Command-M**.

6. In the **To**: box, enter the call sign of the MIM.

7. In the **Msg**: box, enter the telemetry units.

The format for the telemetry units is UNIT.C1,C2,C3,C4,C5,D1,D2,D3,D4,D5,D6,D7, where C1 through C5 are the units for analog ports and D1 through D7 are the labels for the bits (for example, UNIT.Ft,Deg,In,V). The maximum length of each unit is 9 characters for C1, 8 characters for C2, 6 each for C3 through C5, 5 each for D1 through D3, and 4 each for D4 through D7.

8. Click on the **OK** button.

9. Select **New Message...** from the **Windows** menu or enter **Command-M**.

10. In the **To**: box, enter the call sign of the MIM.

11. In the **Msg**: box, enter the telemetry equations.

The format for the telemetry equations is EQNS. E1,F1,G1,E2,F2,G2,E3,F3,G3,E4,F4,G4,E5,F5,G5 where E1 through E5, F1 through F5, and G1 through G5 are the coefficients of a quadratic equation for each of the five analog channels (for example, EQNS.0.53,0,0,0). The quadratic equation is $H = EJ^2 + FJ + G$ where H is the final value and J is the value transmitted by the MIM.

12.Click on the **OK** button.

13.Select **New Message...** from the **Windows** menu or enter **Command-M**.

14.In the **To**: box, enter the call sign of the MIM.

15.In the **Msg**: box, enter the digital bit definitions and the project name.

The format for the digital bit definitions and the project name is BITS.KKKKKKKK,L where KKKKKKKK indicates whether the on-state of each of the digital inputs is represented by a 0 or 1 and where L is the name of the project up to 23 characters in length (for example, BITS.10110000,Horzepa's Zeppelin).

16. Click on the **OK** button.

# Displaying Telemetry

The following describes how to display received telemetry with APRSdos and MacAPRS. WinAPRS does not support the reception of telemetry.

## APRSdos

To display received telemetry with APRSdos, enter **Alt-T**.

If your station has successfully received the four messages intended to set up the telemetry scenario, the **Telemetry** window appears (similar to the window illustrated in Figure 12-1) and begins displaying telemetry received over the air.

The **SER** and **TIME** fields appear in all **Telemetry** list windows. The other fields, including the name of the project (in this example, Horzepa's Zeppelin), are dependent on the contents of the messages transmitted by the station designated to initialize the telemetry scenario. **SER** and **TIME** indicate a sequential number assigned to each telemetry packet and time each packet was received from the MIM.

## MacAPRS

To display received telemetry with MacAPRS, select **Telemetry List** from the **Windows** menu, and the **Telemetry List** window appears and begins displaying telemetry received over the air.

CHAPTER 13

# Monitoring DX Clusters

Today, the DX cluster is arguably the most popular packet radio application. It is also the most inefficient.

The primary function of the DX cluster is to relay current DX information to all the stations that are logged onto the cluster. When one station sends a DX spot, that is, information about a currently active DX station, to the cluster, the cluster relays that information to each station on the cluster. If 25 stations are logged on, this results in the transmission of a minimum of 50 packets! The cluster transmits one packet containing the DX spot to each of the 25 stations on the cluster and each of these 25 stations transmits a packet back to the cluster acknowledging the receipt of the DX spot packet.

APRS offers a more efficient way of accomplishing this primary function of the DX cluster. If the majority of stations monitoring a cluster used APRS instead of logging onto the cluster, the cluster would only send DX spot packets to the minority of stations logged onto the cluster. Yet, all the stations, those logged onto the cluster and those monitoring the cluster with APRS, would receive the DX spots.

For example, if 20 stations are monitoring the cluster with APRS and 5 other stations are logged onto the cluster, each time a DX spot occurs the cluster sends a DX spot packet to each of the 5 stations on the cluster and each of these 5 stations transmits a packet back to the cluster acknowledging the receipt of the DX spot packet for a total of 10 packets. However, the 20 stations monitoring the cluster with APRS will also receive the DX spot, so in effect the transmission of 10 packets in a DX cluster with APRS accomplishes the same task as 50 packets in a DX cluster without APRS described two paragraphs earlier. That is a big (5 to 1) improvement in packet efficiency without any loss in functionality. In reality, only three stations need to be connected to the cluster in order for this system to work, so even greater efficiency may be achieved.

Both APRSdos and MacAPRS support DX cluster monitoring and APRSdos is especially DX cluster monitoring friendly. It not only displays the DX spot information as text, but it also displays it graphically by indicating the approximate location of each DX spot on its world map, as illustrated in Figure 13-1.

In addition to tracking DX spots, APRSdos also performs other DX cluster monitoring functions such as sounding out each DX call sign and its operating frequency in Morse code; saving each WWV propagation report, weather report, general announcements, and user-to-user chats transmitted on the cluster; and plotting the location of any station that is the subject of the **SHOW/STATION DX** cluster command.

## DX Cluster Monitoring Mode

The following describes how to put APRS in the DX cluster monitoring mode with APRSdos and MacAPRS (WinAPRS does not support DX cluster monitoring operation.)

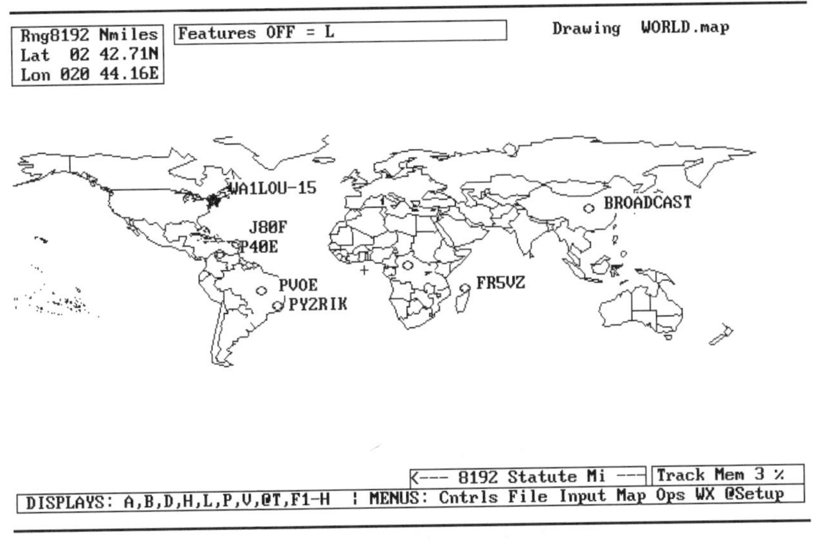


**Figure 13-1—In the DX mode, APRSdos indicates the approximate position of each DX spot on its world map.**

## APRSdos

To put APRSdos in the DX cluster monitoring mode:

1. Enter **Alt-S**.
2. At the **Setup** prompt, enter **M** (for Modes).
3. At the **Modes** prompt, enter **D** (for DX).

To exit the DX cluster monitoring mode with APRSdos:

1. Enter **Alt-S**.
2. At the **Setup** prompt, enter **M** (for Modes).
3. At the **Modes** prompt, enter **D** (for DX) to toggle off the DX mode or enter a letter to select a different mode.

## MacAPRS

To put MacAPRS in the DX cluster monitoring mode, select **DX Cluster Msg Headers** from the Windows menu.

To exit the DX cluster monitoring mode with MacAPRS, deselect **DX Cluster Msg Headers** from the Windows menu.

# DX Information

The following describes how to display the information (DX spots, WWV propagation, weather reports, general announcements, etc.) that are transmitted by stations on the DX cluster channel.

## APRSdos

When APRSdos is in the DX mode, it displays the approximate position of each station that is spotted on a world map. In addition to the graphic representation of each DX spot, there are a number of options in APRSdos for displaying DX information in a text. You may display (1) DX spots, announcements, and weather information, (2) a list of DX mail, (3) the contents of user-to-user chats and (4) the call sign prefixes of every DX "country."

DX Spots, Announcements, and Weather—To display DX information with APRSdos, enter **A**. The window that appears lists the call sign of the station originating the DX spot, the

ALL DX SPOTS, ANNOUNCEMENTS & WEATHER

| DX de SPOTTER | FREQ | DX STATION | COMMENTS | TIME |
|---|---|---|---|---|
| DX de KF8EP: | 14270.0 | BROADCAST | in French | 1834Z |
| DX de VO1SA: | 21026.6 | P40E | | 1845Z |
| DX de KA7YAO-9: | 21027.0 | PVOE | Call correction | 1822Z |
| DX de WA1LNP: | 10102.5 | FR5VZ | | 1838Z |
| DX de KE1FE: | 21027.0 | P40E | CALL CORRECTION | 1836Z |
| DX de VO1SA: | 21270.0 | J80F | | 1849Z |
| DX de KE1FE: | 28380.0 | PY2RIK | nice sig... | 1842Z |

DISPLAYS: A,B,D,H,L,P,V,@T,F1-H | MENUS: Cntrls File Input Map Ops WX @Setup

**Figure 13-2—The DX Spots, Announcements & Weather window of APRSdos lists DX spots transmitted on the DX cluster channel.**

operating frequency of the DX station, the call sign of the DX station, any comments relative to the DX spot, and the time of the DX spot. Figure 13-2 illustrates the All DX Spots, Announcements & Weather window of APRSdos.

To limit the display of DX spots to HF or VHF/UHF DX spots (both as text and graphically):

1. Enter **Alt-F**.

2. Enter **HF** to limit the display of DX spots to HF DX, **VHF** to limit the display to VHF and UHF DX, or **ALL** for unlimited display of DX spots to all DX.

DX Mail—To display a list of the mail on the DX cluster channel, enter **D**. Figure 13-3 illustrates the DX Active Mail Messages Accumulated window of APRSdos.

User-to-User Chats—To display the contents of user-to-user chats that occur on the DX cluster, enter **T**.

DX Prefixes—To display the call sign prefixes of each DX "country" on the APRS map, enter **Alt-A**.

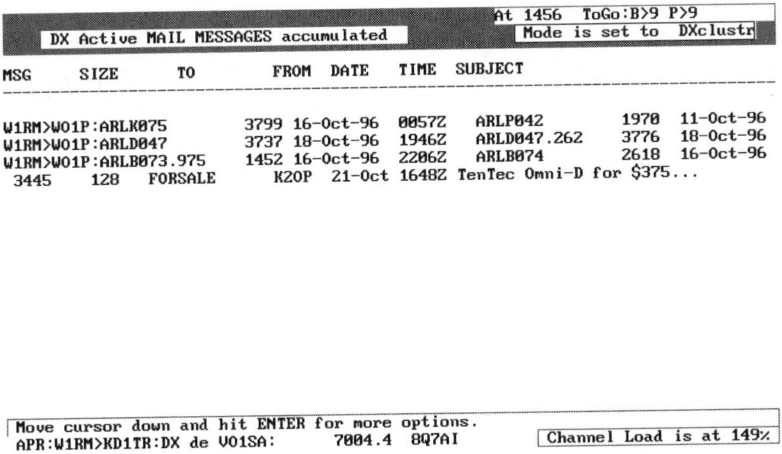

```
                                                    At 1456   ToGo:B>9 P>9
  DX Active MAIL MESSAGES accumulated                Mode is set to  DXclustr

MSG      SIZE      TO          FROM  DATE    TIME  SUBJECT
------------------------------------------------------------------------------

W1RM>WO1P:ARLK075           3799 16-Oct-96  0057Z    ARLP042        1970  11-Oct-96
W1RM>WO1P:ARLD047           3737 18-Oct-96  1946Z    ARLD047.262    3776  18-Oct-96
W1RM>WO1P:ARLB073.975       1452 16-Oct-96  2206Z    ARLB074        2618  16-Oct-96
 3445     128    FORSALE       K2OP  21-Oct 1648Z TenTec Omni-D for $375...




Move cursor down and hit ENTER for more options.
APR:W1RM>KD1TR:DX de VO1SA:      7004.4  8Q7AI            Channel Load is at 149%
```

**Figure 13-3—The DX Active Mail Messages Accumulated window of APRSdos lists the packet mail messages that have been transmitted on the DX cluster channel.**

Figure 13-4 illustrates an APRS map of Africa that includes the call sign prefix of each country on the map.

CW Options—The CW sounding function has a number of options. To access these options, enter **C** (for Controls), then **W** (for cW) and the following list of options appears: **Enable, Disable, Freq(dx), Setspeed, Test**.

Entering **E** or **D** respectively enables or disables the CW sounding option. Entering **F** (for Freq) enables the sounding of the operating frequency of the DX station in addition to the sounding of its call sign. Entering **S** (for Setspeed) allows you to select the CW speed in words-per-minute. Entering **T** (for Test) sends a sample of the CW sounding function as you have configured it.

## MacAPRS

There are two ways of displaying DX information with MacAPRS. Both ways use text (MacAPRS does not display DX spots on its maps as does APRSdos). The primary difference

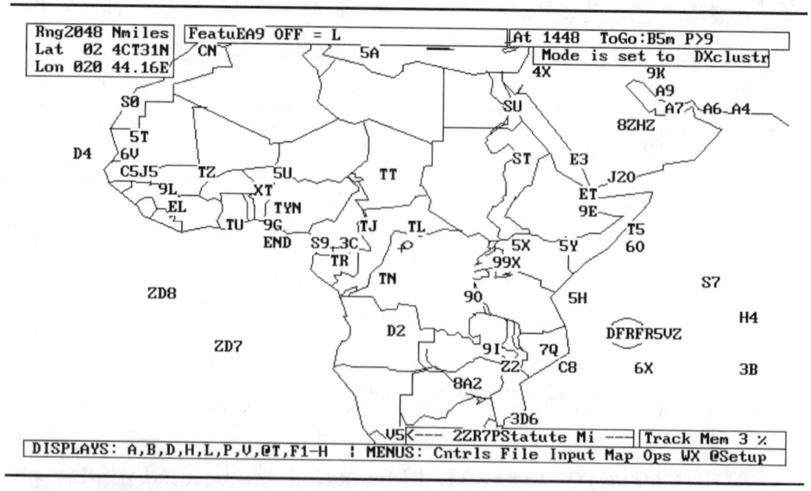


**Figure 13-4—Maps in the APRSdos DX mode may display the call sign prefixes of each DX "country."**

between the two is that the first way includes the call sign of the station originating the DX spot, while the second does not.

1. Enter **Command-2** or select **When List** from the **Windows** menu.

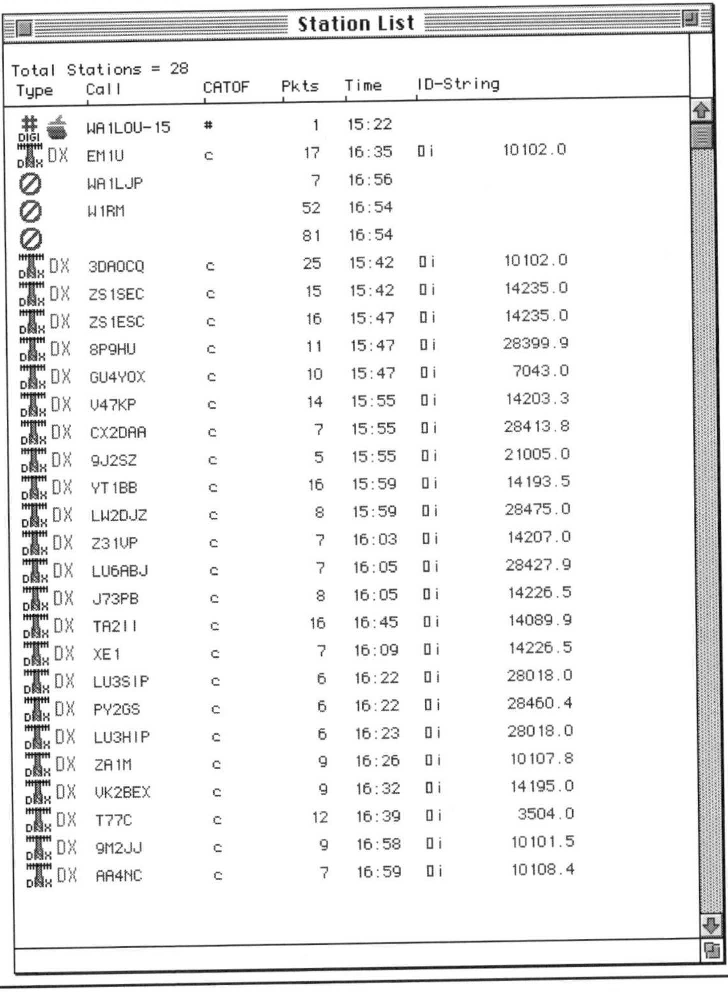

**Station List**

Total Stations = 28

| Type | Call | CATOF | Pkts | Time | ID-String |
|---|---|---|---|---|---|
| DIGI | WA1LOU-15 | # | 1 | 15:22 | |
| DX | EM1U | c | 17 | 16:35 | Di 10102.0 |
| | WA1LJP | | 7 | 16:56 | |
| | W1RM | | 52 | 16:54 | |
| | | | 81 | 16:54 | |
| DX | 3DA0CQ | c | 25 | 15:42 | Di 10102.0 |
| DX | ZS1SEC | c | 15 | 15:42 | Di 14235.0 |
| DX | ZS1ESC | c | 16 | 15:47 | Di 14235.0 |
| DX | 8P9HU | c | 11 | 15:47 | Di 28399.9 |
| DX | GU4YOX | c | 10 | 15:47 | Di 7043.0 |
| DX | V47KP | c | 14 | 15:55 | Di 14203.3 |
| DX | CX2DAA | c | 7 | 15:55 | Di 28413.8 |
| DX | 9J2SZ | c | 5 | 15:55 | Di 21005.0 |
| DX | YT1BB | c | 16 | 15:59 | Di 14193.5 |
| DX | LW2DJZ | c | 8 | 15:59 | Di 28475.0 |
| DX | Z31VP | c | 7 | 16:03 | Di 14207.0 |
| DX | LU6ABJ | c | 7 | 16:05 | Di 28427.9 |
| DX | J73PB | c | 8 | 16:05 | Di 14226.5 |
| DX | TA2II | c | 16 | 16:45 | Di 14089.9 |
| DX | XE1 | c | 7 | 16:09 | Di 14226.5 |
| DX | LU3SIP | c | 6 | 16:22 | Di 28018.0 |
| DX | PY2GS | c | 6 | 16:22 | Di 28460.4 |
| DX | LU3HIP | c | 6 | 16:23 | Di 28018.0 |
| DX | ZA1M | c | 9 | 16:26 | Di 10107.8 |
| DX | UK2BEX | c | 9 | 16:32 | Di 14195.0 |
| DX | T77C | c | 12 | 16:39 | Di 3504.0 |
| DX | 9M2JJ | c | 9 | 16:58 | Di 10101.5 |
| DX | AA4NC | c | 7 | 16:59 | Di 10108.4 |

**Figure 13-5—The Station List window of MacAPRS displays pertinent data concerning each DX spot monitored on the DX cluster channel.**

The following pertinent information is displayed in the **When Station List**: the call sign of the DX station, the approximate time of the DX spot graphically plotted on a chart, the call sign of the station originating the DX spot, and the operating frequency of the DX station.

2. Enter **Command-1** or select **Station List** from the **Windows** menu.

The following pertinent information is displayed in the **Station List**: the call sign of the DX station, the time of the DX spot, and the operating frequency of the DX station, as illustrated in Figure 13-5.

*Appendix A*

# Map-Making

Making maps for APRS usage can be the subject of another book. As a result, this appendix provides you with basic guidance regarding APRS map-making. For details, refer to the documentation that accompanies the various map-making applications.

MAP USAGE RULES

There are three basic rules regarding the compatibility of maps used with the three versions of APRS. They are:

1. APRSdos can only use maps specifically created for APRSdos.
2. MacAPRS can use maps created for MacAPRS, WinAPRS and APRSdos.
3. WinAPRS can use maps created for WinAPRS, MacAPRS and APRSdos.

## DOS Map-Making Software

For APRSdos, you can use the following programs to create maps: *MAKEMAP*, *MAPFIX*, and *MK100K*. These programs are bundled with APRSdos.

*MAKEMAP* is an APRSdos map-making program which allows you to create 32 to 64 mile radius maps by extracting data from the 1:2,000,000 Digital Line Graph (DLG) CD-ROMs that are available from the United States Geological Survey (USGS, Washington, DC 20242).

*MAPFIX* is an APRSdos map-making program which allows you to create maps in any of the following ways: drawing them freehand, drawing them with a digitizer tablet, drawing them by using data generated from an APRS track history file, importing data from other maps, overlaying maps to create new maps, or by extracting data from the 1:2,000,000 or 1:100,000 DLG USGS CD-ROMs.

*MK100K* is an APRSdos map-making program which allows you to create street-level maps by extracting data from the 1:100,000 DLG USGS CD-ROMs. Today, *MK100K* is the program of choice for creating maps from USGS DLG CD-ROMs.

## Macintosh Map-Making Software

For MacAPRS, you can use MacAPRS itself or a program called *MacDLG* to create maps.

MacAPRS has two built-in functions for creating MacAPRS maps: the Convert PC APRS Map File and Merge Map Files functions. They are accessible from the File menu. Convert PC APRS Map File allows you to convert APRSdos maps for compatibility with MacAPRS, as well as WinAPRS. Merge Map Files allows you to create MacAPRS maps, as well as WinAPRS maps, by combining preexisting maps.

*MacDLG* is a Macintosh map-making program that creates MacAPRS and WinAPRS maps from 1:100,000 DLG data obtained from the USGS CD-ROMs, via the Internet by accessing the URL: **http://edcwww.cr.usgs.gov/doc/edchome /ndcdb/ndcdb.html**, or from Census Bureau TIGER map files. *MacDLG* is available from some of the same sources as

MacAPRS. For example, you can ftp *MacDLG* from **ftp.tapr.org, subdirectory /tapr/SIG/aprssig/files/macstuff**.

## Windows Map-Making Software

At this time, there is no WinAPRS map-making software. WinAPRS simply uses maps created with the APRSdos or Macintosh map-making software.

Appendix B

# Glossary of Terms

***address***—the identification of a packet source or destination

***AFSK***—abbreviation for audio-frequency-shift keying

***American National Standard Code for Information Interchange (ASCII)***—a seven bit digital code used in computer and radioteleprinter applications

***AMSAT***—abbreviation for The Radio Amateur Satellite Corporation

***APRS***—abbreviation for Automatic Packet/Position Reporting System

***ASCII***—abbreviation for American National Standard Code for Information Interchange

***asynchronous***—a data transmission timing technique that adds extra bits of information to indicate the beginning and end of each transmitted character

***audio-frequency-shift keying (AFSK)***—a method of transmitting digital information by switching between two audio tones fed into the transmitter audio input

***autobaud***—the ability of a communications device to automatically adapt to whatever data rate is used by the terminal connected to it

***Automatic Packet/Position Reporting System (APRS)***—a packet radio application for tracking real-time events by graphically displaying information on maps displayed on the user's computer screen

***baud***—a unit of signaling speed equal to one pulse (event or symbol) per second in a single-channel transmission

***BBS***—abbreviation for bulletin-board system

***beacon***—a TNC function that permits a station to automatically send unconnected packets at regular intervals

***bit***—binary digit, a signal that is either on/one or off/zero; bits are combined to represent alphanumeric and control characters for data communications

***bulletin-board system (BBS)***—a computer system where messages and files can be stored for other users

***byte***—a group of bits, usually eight in number

***data circuit-terminating equipment, data communications equipment (DCE)***—the device that provides communications between a DTE and radio equipment or telephone lines

***data terminal equipment (DTE)***—a device that is used as an interface between a human and a computer to allow the human to exchange information with the computer

***DCE***—abbreviation for data circuit-terminating equipment and data communications equipment

***default***—the state of a TNC parameter after the TNC is initially turned on or reset

***demodulate***—the process of retrieving information from a modulated carrier

***DF***—abbreviation for direction finding

***digipeater***—digital repeater, a device that receives, temporarily stores and then transmits (repeats) packet radio transmissions that are specifically addressed for routing through the digipeater

***Digital Line Graph (DLG)***—a map data format used for creating APRS maps

***DLG***—abbreviation for Digital Line Graph

***DTE***—abbreviation for data terminal equipment

***DX cluster***—a packet radio system that relays current DX information to all the stations that are logged onto the system

***DX spot***—information concerning a currently active DX station

***EIA***—abbreviation for Electronic Industries Association

***EIA-232***—the EIA standard for DTE-to-DCE (TNC) interfacing that specifies the interface signals and their electrical characteristics

***Electronic Industries Association (EIA)***—an organization composed of representatives of the United States electronics industry; the EIA is involved in formulating data communication standards.

***Enter***—a key on a computer keyboard that causes the computer to accept the information previously typed at its keyboard

***enter***—to use a key (for example, the Enter key) on a computer keyboard to cause the computer to accept the information previously typed at its keyboard

***fade point***—the location where a direction-finding station loses or acquires the signal transmitted by an unknown station

***File Transport Protocol (FTP)***—part of the TCP/IP suite of protocols that allows the user to transfer files to or from the computer at another node

***FTP***—abbreviation for File Transport Protocol

***gateway***—a device or PBBS function that allows packet radio stations on different operating frequencies to communicate with each other

***Global Positioning System (GPS)***—a system that uses orbiting satellites to determine the location of GPS receiving stations on the surface of the Earth

***GPS***—abbreviation for Global Positioning System

***HSP***—abbreviation for Hardware Single Port mode, the mode in APRSdos that permits a single serial port to be shared between a TNC and a GPS using a specialized hardware switch

***MacAPRS***—a version of Automatic Packet/Position Reporting System (APRS) that runs on a Macintosh platform

***MacAPRS for Windows***—also known as WinAPRS, a version of Automatic Packet/Position Reporting System (APRS) that runs on a Windows platform; the Windows version was ported from MacAPRS, the Macintosh version of APRS

***Micro Interface Module (MIM)***—a telemetry TNC in one integrated circuit

***MIM***—abbreviation for Micro Interface Module

***modem***—modulator-demodulator; an electronic device that permits digital equipment to use analog communications media for data communications

***NMEA***—abbreviation for National Marine Electronics Association

***network***—a system of interconnected packet radio stations assembled for the efficient transfer of packets over long distances

***path***—the route between two connected packet radio stations consisting of digipeaters and other packet stations

***port***—a circuit that allows a device to communicate with external devices

***position***—an Unnumbered Information (UI) packet generated by APRS that contains information concerning the location of the APRS station; the latitude and longitude of an APRS station

***The Radio Amateur Satellite Corporation (AMSAT)***—an Amateur Radio organization that is responsible for United States amateur satellite developments

***radio port***—the TNC port that is connected to a radio transceiver (or transmitter and receiver)

***RAM***—abbreviation for random-access memory

***random-access memory (RAM)***—a data storage device that can be written to and read from

***Received Data***—an EIA-232 serial interface signal that consists of data from the DCE (TNC) that was received over the communication medium and demodulated by the DCE (TNC)

***secondary station identifier (SSID)***—a number that follows a packet radio station call sign to differentiate between two or more packet radio stations operating under the same call sign

***Send Data***—an EIA-232 serial interface signal that consists of data from a DTE that is intended for transmission by the DCE (TNC) over the communication medium; also called Transmitted Data

***serial***—the transfer of bit-encoded information bit-by-bit

***serial interface, serial port***—an interconnection that transfers bit-encoded information bit-by-bit (serially); the TNC connection for a terminal or computer

***Signal Ground***—an EIA-232 serial interface signal that provides a common ground reference for all the other interface signals except Shield (pin 1)

***SPM***—abbreviation for Single Port Mode, in APRSdos a mode that will accept both TNC and GPS formatted data on the same serial port

***SSID***—abbreviation for secondary station identifier

***station type***—a specific station category in APRS operation

***stop bit***—one or two extra bits that follow a character to indicate its end in asynchronous data communications

***TAPR***—abbreviation for Tucson Amateur Packet Radio Corporation

***terminal***—short for data terminal equipment or a computer emulating data terminal equipment

***terminal node controller (TNC)***—an Amateur Radio packet assembler/disassembler; may or may not include a modem

***TNC***—abbreviation for terminal-node controller

***TNC 1***—the first TAPR TNC that was made available to the general public; it was based on the 6809 microprocessor

***TNC 2***—the second TAPR TNC that was made available to the general public; based on a Z80 microprocessor; its design was the most popular in amateur packet radio history

***Transmitted Data***—an EIA-232 serial interface signal that consists of data from a DTE that is intended for transmission by the DCE (TNC) over the communication medium; also called Send Data

***Tucson Amateur Packet Radio Corporation (TAPR)***—the Arizona-based Amateur Radio organization that was instrumental in packet radio protocol and hardware development in the United States

***UI***—abbreviation for Unnumbered Information frame

***unconnected packets***—packets transmitted from a source station with no specific destination station being addressed; used for beacons, CQs, and round table communications

***United States Geological Survey (USGS)***—a federal agency which is a source for map data used for creating APRS maps

***Unnumbered Information (UI)***—an AX.25 unnumbered frame that allows data to be transmitted from a source station with no specific destination station being addressed

***upload***—to send files to a PBBS or other packet radio station

***USGS***—abbreviation for United States Geological Survey

***wide digipeater***—an APRS digipeater that is well-situated in order to provide coverage of wide expanses of an APRS network

***WinAPRS***—also known as MacAPRS for Windows, a version of Automatic Packet/Position Reporting System (APRS) that runs on a Windows platform; the Windows version was ported from MacAPRS, the Macintosh version of APRS

## Appendix C

# Commands

The following tables list and briefly describe all the commands in the three versions of APRS.

Most APRSdos commands are entered by typing the uppercase characters in the command name, for example, to enter the **All** command, you type the letter **A**, to enter the **Controls - cW - Disable** command, you type **C**, then **W**, and **D**. A few APRSdos commands are entered by typing a number (e.g., 9), pressing a control-character (e.g., [**Home**]), or pressing a function-key (e.g., [**Function-5**]). The APRSdos Description column lists the default of the command, if any, in brackets (e.g., [off]).

Most MacAPRS and WinAPRS commands are entered by selecting a command from a pull-down menu or pull-down sub-menu, for example, to enter the **Edit - Clear Stations and Messages** command, you pull down the **Edit** menu and select **Clear Stations and Messages**. A few MacAPRS and WinAPRS commands are entered by typing a control-character (e.g., [**Home**]).

Some MacAPRS and WinAPRS commands have keyboard shortcuts which are listed in brackets (e.g., [**Cmd-O**] and [**F-S**]) in the Menu Command column. You enter most MacAPRS shortcuts by holding down the **Command** key and pressing a second key. For example, to use the [**Cmd-O**] shortcut, you press the **O** key while holding down the **Command** key. You enter most WinAPRS shortcuts by typing one key and then typing a second key. For example, to use the [**F-S**] shortcut, you type **F**, then **S**.

## APRSdos Commands

| *Keyboard Command* | *Description [default, if any]* |
|---|---|
| 1 | show default map |
| 3 | show map saved for key 3 |
| 5 | show map saved for key 5 |
| 7 | show map saved for key 7 |
| 9 | show map saved for key 9 |
| All | show all received messages and beacons in chronological order |
| Bulletins | show last 22 received bulletins |
| Controls - Bands - 2port | configure APRSdos for dual-port TNC operation |
| Controls - Bands - Hf | configure APRSdos for HF TNC operation |
| Controls - Bands - Vhf | configure APRSdos for VHF/UHF TNC operation |
| Controls - cW - Disable | disables sounding received beacons in CW |
| Controls - cW - Enable | enables sounding received beacons in CW [off] |
| Controls - cW - Freq | in DX mode, enables/disables sounding DX frequencies in CW [off] |
| Controls - cW - Setspeed | select words-per-minute of CW soundings [15] |
| Controls - cW - Test | test CW sounding function |
| Controls - Dr | turn on/off dead reckoning [off] |
| Controls - Filters - Direct | turn on/off filtering digipeated stations [off] |
| Controls - Filter - Dx | in DX mode, select filters for HF, VHF and certain bands |
| Controls - Filters - Fadegray | turn on/off filtering currently inactive stations [on] |
| Controls - Filters - Hfgate | turn on/off filtering gateway stations [off] |
| Controls - Filters - Junk | turn on/off filtering data embedded with control characters |
| Controls - Filters - Other | turn on/off filtering non-beacon packets [on] |
| Controls - Filters - Posfltr | turn on/off filtering of random GPS data errors [on] |
| Controls - Filters - !Fixed | turn on/off filtering of fixed stations [on] |
| Controls - K/m | select map measurements in kilometers or miles [miles] |
| Controls - Log | turn on/off automatic logging of track histories [off] |

| | |
|---|---|
| Controls - Other | turn on/off display of non-APRS packets |
| Controls - Uplinks | turn on/off transmitting your object data [on] |
| Controls - Xmt | turn on/off normal transmitting [off] |
| Digis | show digipeaters used by all received stations |
| Erase | delete transmitted messages |
| File - Append | load a backup file without losing current station data |
| File - Dos | transfer to DOS |
| File - Load | load a backup file |
| File - Maplists | show directory of available Maplist files |
| File - Orderlists | sort station list in chronological order with oldest stations first |
| File - Print | select data for printing |
| File - Replay | load and play saved track history files |
| File - Save | save current data |
| File - Zeromem | clear memory of all data |
| Goto | move cursor to your station or tracked station |
| Heard | show packets per hour received from each station during previous 24 hours |
| Inputs - Addobj | add an object to the APRS map at the current cursor position |
| Inputs - Df | enter a beam heading or signal report for direction finding |
| Inputs - Heading | enter the direction of your vehicle |
| Inputs - Mypos | enter the position of your station |
| Inputs - Pwrhtgain | enter the transmitter power and antenna parameters of your station |
| Inputs - Savemy | save the current position of your station as an object |
| Inputs - Upmy | transmit the current position of your station and save it as an object |
| Just - All | clear map and show all stations |
| Just - Both m&w | clear map and show only moving and weather stations |
| Just - Calls | clear map and show only station symbols |
| Just - Latest | clear map and show only latest stations |
| Just - Mobiles | clear map and show only moving stations |
| Just - Onesymbol - Antenna | clear map and show only stations using selectable antenna symbol |
| Just - Onesymbol - Bldings | clear map and show only stations using selectable building symbol |

| | |
|---|---|
| Just - Onesymbol - Df | clear map and show only stations using selectable direction finding symbol |
| Just - Onesymbol - Mobiles | clear map and show only stations using selectable mobiles symbol |
| Just - Onesymbol - Objects | clear map and show only stations using selectable objects symbol |
| Just - Onesymbol - Packet | clear map and show only stations using selectable packet symbol |
| Just - Onesymbol - Special | clear map and show only stations using selectable special symbol |
| Just - Onesymbol - Wx | clear map and show only stations using selectable weather symbol |
| Just - Print | print or save positions list |
| Just - Special | clear map and show only stations using special symbols |
| Just - Types | clear map and show only APRSdos stations |
| Just - Wx | clear map and show only weather stations |
| Kill | delete received messages |
| Latest | show latest received messages |
| Map - Alt | show map, if any, under currently displayed map |
| Map - Change | change the currently selected Maplist |
| Map - Config - Offset | align map with GPS data |
| Map - Dn | magnify map |
| Map - Features - *rr | turn on/off display of railroads on map [on] |
| Map - Features - All | turn on/off display of all map features [on] |
| Map - Features - Brdrs | turn on/off display of map |
| Map - Features - Calls | turn on/off display of call signs on map [on] |
| Map - Features - Dim | turn on/off dimmed map display [off] |
| Map - Features - Headings | turn on/off display of headings on map [on] |
| Map - Features - Labels | turn on/off display of labels on map [on] |
| Map - Features - Roads | turn on/off display of roads on map [on] |
| Map - Features - Tint | change background color of map |
| Map - Features - Water | turn on/off display of waterways on map [on] |
| Map - Home | center map at current cursor position |
| Map - Loc | lock currently displayed map to override automatic map selection function |
| Map - Ovrlay | overlay larger map over current map |
| Map - Overlay | other select map overlay |

| | |
|---|---|
| Map - Plots - Borders | show perimeters of all selectable maps |
| Map - Plots - Calls | show call sign prefixes on map for all countries |
| Map - Plots - Cap | overlay Civil Air Patrol grid squares on map |
| Map - Plots - Df | show coverage circles representing reported signal strengths of unknown source |
| Map - Plots - Fadedf | show calculated location of unknown radio signal based on fade points |
| Map - Plots - Gridsq | overlay 2-character Maidenhead grid squares on map |
| Map - Plots - Heard | show only direction finding stations reporting a signal from unknown source |
| Map - Plots - Nothrd | show only direction finding stations reporting no signal from unknown source |
| Map - Plots - Overlaps | show map hierarchy |
| Map - Plots - Pwrhtgn | show circles representing station coverage area |
| Map - Plots - Rngrngs | show coverage circles at 1, 3/4, 1/2, and 1/4 of the coverage circle scale |
| Map - Save | save current map for recall with function keys 3, 5, 7, or 9 |
| Map - Up | reduce map |
| Map - Which | show name of map |
| Next | move cursor to next weather station and show its weather data |
| Operations - Communicate - Df | open window for direct communications with direction finding equipment |
| Operations - Communicate - Gps | open window for direct communications with GPS equipment |
| Operations - Communicate - Tnc | open window for direct communications with TNC |
| Operations - Communicate - Wx | open window for direct communications with weather station equipment |
| Operations - Digipath | save 1 to 12 digipeater paths for later recall |
| Operations - Digipeater - Enter | configure the normal digipeater path for your station |
| Operations - Find | find a call sign or grid square on a map or in a list |
| Operations - Ping | transmit a test packet via the current digipeater path |
| Operations - Query | transmit an APRS query packet |
| Operations - Replaytrks | play a track history |
| Operations - Setradar | sets a penetration range alarm |
| Operations - Unprotovia | configure the normal digipeater path for your station |
| Positions | show received APRS position packets |
| Quit | quit APRSdos |
| Quit - [Escape | exit APRSdos without saving |

| Quit - eXit | exit APRSdos using 2-key default |
|---|---|
| Read | show transmitted and received messages |
| Send | create and transmit message or bulletin |
| Traffic | show last 23 lines of received traffic |
| Unproto | configure the normal digipeater path for your station |
| View | show scrolling list of all received packets |
| Weather - Alarms - Clearalarm | clear weather alarms |
| Weather - Alarms - Hight | configure high temperature alarm |
| Weather - Alarms - Lowt | configure low temperature alarm |
| Weather - Alarms - Rain | configure rain alarm |
| Weather - Alarms - rAnge | limit weather alarms from stations within a selectable distance |
| Weather - Alarms - Wind | configure wind alarm |
| Weather - Alarms - Zerorn | set the rain gauge measurement to 0 |
| Weather - Displays - Baro | show atmospheric pressure and time of report |
| Weather - Displays - Calls | show call signs of weather stations |
| Weather - Displays - Justw | limit map display to weather stations |
| Weather - Displays - Otherwxsyms | turn on/off alternate weather symbols [off] |
| Weather - Displays - Temps | show temperature and rainfall reading |
| Weather - Displays - Winds | show wind speed and rainfall readings and time of report |
| Weather - Get - Metar | update position list with the latest METAR data |
| Weather - Log | turn on/off saving weather reports to track history |
| Weather - Metric | use metric system for weather station data |
| Weather - Nws - Addnwsstnstoplist | enter NWS stations located on current map to Positions list |
| Weather - Nws - Loadnwsdata | load file containing hourly NWS data |
| Weather - Nws - Shownwsstns | show NWS stations on current map |
| Weather - Query | transmit an APRS weather station query packet |
| Xmt - All | transmit all your outstanding packets |
| Xmt - Beacon | transmit all your outstanding beacon packets |
| Xmt - bUlletin | transmit all your outstanding bulletin packets |
| Xmt - Messages | transmit all your outstanding message packets |

|  |  |
| --- | --- |
| Xmt - Objects | transmit all your outstanding objects packets |
| Xmt - Posit | transmit all your outstanding position packets |
| Yaxis | turn on/off 3-dimensional display of currently selected map |
| [Alt-B] | change beacon text |
| [Alt-S] - Df - dfJr | turn on/off DFjr mode [off] |
| [Alt-S] - Df - Dfsp | turn on/off DFSP mode [off] |
| [Alt-S] - Formats - Mscatter | turn on/off meteor scatter mode [off] |
| [Alt-S] - Formats - Normalaprs | turn on/off normal APRS operation [on] |
| [Alt-S] - Formats - Space | turn on/off spacecraft mode [off] |
| [Alt-S] - Gps - Modes | select GPS mode |
| [Alt-S] - Gps - Off/ongps | disable SPM or HSP |
| [Alt-S] - Gps - Plot | show plot of GPS satellites and their signal strengths |
| [Alt-S] - Gps - Timesync | set system clock from local NMEA/GPS equipment |
| [Alt-S] - Gps - Waypoint | upload position packets to GPS |
| [Alt-S] - Modes - altNet | turn on/off special function net mode [off] |
| [Alt-S] - Modes - Autospace | turn on/off automatic spacecraft mode [off] |
| [Alt-S] - Modes - Dx | turn on/off DX mode [off] |
| [Alt-S] - Modes - Master | configure the computer as a master where multiple computers share one TNC |
| [Alt-S] - Modes - Pseudo | make differential correction with GPS |
| [Alt-S] - Modes - slaVe | configure the computer as a slave where multiple computers share one TNC |
| [Alt-S] - Modes - Special | turn on/off special event mode [off] |
| [Alt-S] - Other - Avggndlvl | enter the height above average terrain (HAAT) of your station |
| [Alt-S] - Other - Beeps | turn on/off APRS sound [on] |
| [Alt-S] - Other - Ega | turn on/off EGA monitor operation [off] |
| [Alt-S] - Other - Game | play chess with APRSdos |
| [Alt-S] - Other - Redraw | select rate of screen redraw |
| [Alt-S] - Other - Scrnsavr | enables/disables screen saver function [off] |
| [Alt-S] - Other - Zone | change time zone of your station |
| [Alt-S] - Posrate | select display and sending rates for GPS, weather and direction finding data |
| [Alt-S] - Save | save current map and configuration |

| | |
|---|---|
| [Alt-S] - Tnc | configure TNC with TNC APRS parameters |
| [Alt-T] | show received telemetry data |
| [Down Arrow] | move cursor down |
| [End] | center map on the default location of your station |
| [Enter] | select (hook) an object |
| [Escape] | move cursor to center of map |
| [Function-1] | show APRSdos help |
| [Function-2] | create and transmit reply to last received message |
| [Function-3] | show more map labels |
| [Function-4] | show fewer map labels |
| [Function-5] | enter fade point for omni-directional direction finding |
| [Function-6] | configure the speed of your mobile station to 0 |
| [Function-7] | select low (23-line) or high (43-line) resolution display [low] |
| [Function-8] | plot an immediate fix in GPS/HSP mode |
| [Function-9] | adjust map size to show all stations |
| [Function-10] | turn on/off Windows mode [disabled] |
| [Home] | center map at current cursor position |
| [Insert] | move selected (hooked) object |
| [Left Arrow] | move cursor left |
| [Page Down] | magnify map |
| [Page Up] | reduce map |
| [Right Arrow] | move cursor right |
| [Space Bar] | show currently selected map |
| [Tab] | show status of Control and Setup command parameters |
| [Up Arrow] | move cursor up |

## MacAPRS Commands

| Menu Command [Keyboard Shortcut] | Description |
|---|---|
| File - New... | open new default map window |
| File - Open File... [Cmd-O] | open file |
| File - Open Call Sign File... | open call sign file |
| File - Open Weather File... | open weather file |
| File - Close Window [Cmd-W] | close active window |
| File - Save... [Cmd-S] | save file |
| File - Get Map Info [Cmd-I] | show map data near bottom of map |
| File - Page Setup... | configure print job |
| File - Print... [Cmd-P] | print active window |
| File - Convert PC APRS Map File... | transform APRSdos maps for MacAPRS compatibility |
| File - Merge Map Files... | combine maps to create new map |
| File - Quit [Cmd-Q] | quit MacAPRS |
| Edit - Undo [Cmd-Z] | not implemented |
| Edit - Cut [Cmd-X] | not implemented |
| Edit - Copy [Cmd-C] | not implemented |
| Edit - Paste [Cmd-V] | not implemented |
| Edit - Clear | not implemented |
| Edit - Select All [Cmd-A] | not implemented |
| Edit - Copy Map | not implemented |
| Edit - Find... [Cmd-F] | locate data on map |
| Edit - Find Again... [Cmd-G] | repeat Edit - Find command |
| Edit - Calculate Distance... [Cmd-=] | determine distance and antenna bearing |
| Edit - Edit/Add Station/Object... [Cmd-E] | add or change station or object on map |
| Edit - Edit/Add Weather Object... | add or change weather object on map |
| Edit - Clear Stations and Messages | delete received station information and messages |
| Edit - Clear Wind Data | delete received wind information |

| | |
|---|---|
| Edit - Clear Region Search Index | not implemented |
| Settings - Master Mode - Normal Ham Operation | configure software for normal APRS operation |
| Settings - Master Mode - Weather ONLY | configure software for APRS weather station operation |
| Settings - Station Settings... | configure MacAPRS with station parameters |
| Settings - Select TNC Type... | configure software for selected TNC type |
| Settings - TNC Settings... | configure MacAPRS with TNC parameters |
| Settings - Position Report Rate Settings... | configure rate of position packet transmissions |
| Settings - GPS Settings... | configure MacAPRS with NMEA/GPS equipment parameters |
| Settings - MacAPRS Settings... | configure MacAPRS with APRS parameters |
| Settings - Data Base Settings... | configure CD-ROM call sign directory |
| Settings - Radio Settings... | not implemented |
| Settings - Weather Settings... | configure MacAPRS with weather station equipment parameters |
| Settings - Sound Settings... | configure MacAPRS sound options |
| Settings - Balloon Settings... | configure MacAPRS with balloon settings |
| Settings - Communications... - HF (or Dual Port) TNC | configure serial port connected to HF TNC |
| Settings - Communications... - VHF TNC | configure serial port connected to VHF/UHF TNC |
| Settings - Communications... - NMEA/GPS | configure serial port connected to NMEA/GPS equipment |
| Settings - Communications... - Weather | configure serial port connected to weather station equipment |
| Settings - Communications... - Direction Finding | configure serial port connected to direction finding equipment |
| Settings - Communications... - Radio Control | not implemented |
| Settings - Communications... - not used | not implemented |
| Settings - Communications... - Binary Input | not implemented |
| Settings - Communications... - Receive Only (TCP/IP) | configure serial port |
| Settings - Communications... - Echo Port | configure serial port |
| Settings - TNC Commands - Send Position [Cmd-T] | transmit beacon packet |
| Settings - TNC Commands - Send Objects | transmit objects packet |
| Settings - TNC Commands - Send Grid-Square Position [Cmd-,] | transmit Maidenhead grid square packet |
| Settings - TNC Commands - Send Weather Report | ransmit weather report packet |
| Settings - TNC Commands - Send RDF Report | transmit direction finding packet |
| Settings - TNC Commands - Send APRS Query [Cmd-/] | ransmit APRS query packet |

|  |  |
| --- | --- |
| Settings - TNC Commands - Send WX Query | transmit an APRS weather station query packet |
| Settings - TNC Commands - Send UNPROTO VIA... [Cmd-U] | configure Unproto VHF/UHF or HF path |
| Settings - TNC Commands - VHF TNC - Re-Initialize TNC | configure HF TNC with TNC Settings parameters |
| Settings - TNC Commands - VHF TNC - Exit KISS Mode | force HF TNC to quit KISS mode |
| Settings - TNC Commands - VHF TNC - Exit Kantronics Host Mode | force HF TNC to quit Kantronics TNC host mode |
| Settings - TNC Commands - VHF TNC - Exit AEA Host Mode | force HF TNC to quit AEA TNC host mode |
| Settings - TNC Commands - HF TNC - Re-Initialize TNC | configure VHF/UHF TNC with TNC Settings parameters |
| Settings - TNC Commands - HF TNC - Exit KISS Mode | force VHF/UHF TNC to quit KISS mode |
| Settings - TNC Commands - HF TNC - Exit Kantronics Host Mode | force VHF/UHF TNC to quit Kantronics TNC host mode |
| Settings - TNC Commands - HF TNC - Exit AEA Host Mode | force VHF/UHF TNC to quit AEA TNC host mode |
| Settings - Unproto APRSM via (HF) - -none- | configure no Unproto HF path |
| Settings - Unproto APRSM via (HF) - Default | configure Unproto HF path with default |
| Settings - Unproto APRS via (HF) - Relay | configure Unproto HF path as Relay |
| Settings - Unproto APRSM via (HF) - Wide | configure Unproto HF path as Wide |
| Settings - Unproto APRSM via (HF) - Wide,Wide | configure Unproto HF path as Wide,Wide |
| Settings - Unproto APRSM via (HF) - Gate,Wide | configure Unproto HF path as Gate,Wide |
| Settings - Unproto APRSM via (HF) - Wide,Gate,Gate,Wide | configure Unproto HF path as Wide,Gate,Gate,Wide |
| Settings - Unproto APRSM via (HF) - Gate,Gate,Wide | configure Unproto HF path as Gate,Gate,Wide |
| Settings - Unproto APRSM via (HF) - Gate,wide\Wide,gate,gate,wide | configure Unproto HF path as Gate,wide\Wide,gate,gate,wide |
| Settings - Unproto APRSM via (VHF) - -none- | configure no Unproto VHF/UHF path |
| Settings - Unproto APRSM via (VHF) - Default | configure Unproto VHF/UHF path with default |
| Settings - Unproto APRS via (VHF) - Relay | configure Unproto VHF path as Relay |
| Settings - Unproto APRSM via (VHF) - Wide | configure Unproto VHF/UHF path as Wide |
| Settings - Unproto APRSM via (VHF) - Wide,Wide | configure Unproto VHF/UHF path as Wide,Wide |
| Settings - Unproto APRSM via (VHF) - Gate,Wide | configure Unproto VHF/UHF path as Gate,Wide |
| Settings - Unproto APRSM via (VHF) - Wide,Gate,Gate,Wide | configure Unproto VHF/UHF path as Wide,Gate,Gate,Wide |
| Settings - Unproto APRSM via (VHF) - Gate,Gate,Wide | configure Unproto VHF/UHF path as Gate,Gate,Wide |

|  |  |
|---|---|
| Settings - Unproto APRSM via (VHF) - Gate,wide\Wide,gate,gate,wide | configure Unproto VHF/UHF path as Gate,wide\Wide,gate,gate,wide |
| Settings - HF TNC (Dual Port) | turn on/off communications with HF TNC |
| Settings - VHF TNC | turn on/off communications with VHF/UHF TNC |
| Settings - GPS/NMEA | turn on/off communications with NMEA/GPS equipment |
| Settings - Weather Station | turn on/off communications with weather station equipment |
| Settings - Direction Finding | turn on/off communications with direction finding equipment |
| Settings - Hard Copy Logging | turn on/off logging to printer |
| Settings - Radio Control | not implemented |
| Settings - TNC via TCP/IP | turn on/off TNC via TCP/IP function |
| Settings - Echo Port | turn on/off echo port function |
| Settings - Stop All Input | disable all input |
| Settings - Flag All Macs | turn on/off the noting of received stations using Macintosh computers |
| Settings - Flag All Windows | turn on/off the noting of received stations using Windows computers |
| Settings - GPS Alarm | turn on/off local NMEA/GPS equipment alarm |
| Settings - SetTime from GPS [Cmd-\] | turn on/off setting system clock from local NMEA/GPS equipment |
| Settings - GPS Setup... | turn on/off local NMEA/GPS equipment checksum calculations |
| Logging - Station Logging | turn on/off recording received station data |
| Logging - APRS Logging | turn on/off recording received APRS data |
| Logging - NMEA Logging | turn on/off recording received NMEA/GPS data |
| Logging - Local Weather Logging | turn on/off recording received weather reports |
| Logging - Message Logging | turn on/off recording received messages |
| Logging - Local RDF Logging | turn on/off recording received direction finding data |
| Logging - Binary GPS Logging | turn on/off recording received binary GPS data |
| Logging - Statistics Logging | turn on/off recording statistics |
| Logging - Stop All Logging | disable recording all received data |
| Map - | select map for display |
| Display - Station Display Mode - Display All Stations (Normal) | show all stations on map |
| Display - Station Display Mode - Direct Stations Only | only show directly-received stations on map |
| Display - Station Display Mode - Flagged Stations Only | only show flagged stations on map |
| Display - Station Display Mode - Tracked Stations Only | only show tracked stations on map |

| | |
|---|---|
| Display - Station Display Mode - Weather Stations Only | only show weather stations on map |
| Display - Map Display Options... | select map display options |
| Display - Home View (Home) [Cmd-H] | show current map in its default size |
| Display - Clear/Redraw | erase deleted map data and redraw map |
| Display - Center View | position center of map at mouse pointer location |
| Display - Zoom In 2x (Page Down) [Page Down] | magnify map by factor of 2 |
| Display - Zoom In 4x | magnify map by factor of 4 |
| Display - Zoom Out 2x (Page Up) [Page Up] | reduce map by factor of 2 |
| Display - Map Boundaries | show perimeters of all selectable maps |
| Display - Overlays... - Display Overlay | select map overlay |
| Display - Overlays... - Display Overlay List | show list of available map overlays |
| Display - Grid Square (2 Ltr) | overlay 2-character Maidenhead grid squares on map |
| Display - Grid Square (4 Ltr) | overlay 4-character Maidenhead grid squares on map |
| Display - Grid Square (6 Ltr) | overlay 6-character Maidenhead grid squares on map |
| Display - Lat/Lon Lines | overlay lines of latitude and longitude |
| Display - C.A.P. 15' Grids | not implemented |
| Display - Display Icons | turn on/off display of icons on map |
| Display - Display Call Signs | turn on/off display of call signs on map |
| Display - Display Labels | turn on/off display of labels on map |
| Display - Display Symbols | turn on/off display of symbols on map |
| Display - Display Filled Polygons | turn on/off display of filled polygons |
| Display - Display APRS Info (Bottom of Screen) | turn on/off display of APRS data near bottom of map |
| Display - Display NMEA Info (Bottom of Screen) | turn on/off display of NMEA/GPS data near bottom of map |
| Display - Display Course & Speed Vectors | turn on/off display of course and speed vectors of moving objects on map |
| Display - Display Dead Reckoning | turn on/off display of dead reckoning data |
| Display - Auto Scroll Moving Map | turn on/off automatic scrolling map function |
| Display - Display Airports | not implemented |
| Display - Display Zip Code | not implemented |
| Display - Display Coverage Circles [Cmd-D] | show circles representing station coverage area |
| Display - Display RDF Intersections | show received direction finding intersections |

| | |
|---|---|
| Display - Replay Selected Station [Cmd-R] | show course of tracked station on map |
| Display - Enable Deleted Stations | enable deleted stations |
| Display - Delete Old Stations | delete old stations |
| Lists - New Message | create and transmit new message or bulletin |
| Lists - Message List | show transmitted and received messages and bulletins |
| Lists - Map List | show all selectable maps |
| Lists - Station List | show received stations' data |
| Lists- Position List | show received stations' location data |
| Lists - When Heard | show list and graph of times that stations were received |
| Lists - Weather List | show received weather data |
| Lists - Shelter List | show received shelters' data |
| Lists - Flagged Station Lists | show received flagged stations' data |
| Lists - Track List | show received tracked stations' data |
| Lists - Mic Enc List | show received MicEncoder stations' data |
| Lists - RDF List | show received direction finding stations' data |
| Lists - ProtoPath List | show received stations' unproto path |
| Lists - History List | show all received packets |
| Lists - CallBook List | show CD-ROM call sign directory entries |
| Lists - Icon List | show MacAPRS symbols and icons |
| Lists - Global Label List | show global labels |
| Lists - Internal State | show MacAPRS configuration data |
| Lists - Packet Statistics | show received packet data |
| Lists - DX Countries List | show "DX" countries of the world |
| Lists - IOTA Lis | show islands of the world |
| Lists - APRS Statistics | show graphic representing packet activity for previous day,week, year |
| Lists - Weather Display | show graphic representing local weather station equipment data |
| Lists - 24hr Weather Charts | show graphic representing local weather data for previous 24 hours |
| Lists - NMEA Display | show graphic representing local NMEA/GPS equipment data |
| Lists - Altitude Statistics | show graphic representing received altitude data |
| Lists - Wind Interpolation | show graphic representing wind interpolation |
| Windows - Next Window [Cmd-'] | deselect active window and select an inactive window |

| | |
|---|---|
| Windows - New Map Window Square [Cmd-N] | open new empty map window |
| Windows - New Map Window Polar | open new map window with polar projection of default map |
| Windows - Close All Windows | close all open windows |
| Windows - Stack Windows | arrange map windows in a stack |
| Windows - Tile Windows | arrange map windows side-by-side |
| Windows - (map name) | show (map name) map |

## WinAPRS Commands

| Menu Command [Keyboard Shortcut] | Description |
|---|---|
| File - About WinAPRS [F-A] | how information about WinAPRS |
| File - Open [F-O] | open file |
| File - Open Weather | open weather file |
| File - Save [F-S] | not implemented |
| File - Close [F-C] | close active opened window |
| File - Print | not implemented |
| File - Exit [F-X] | quit WinAPRS |
| Edit - Copy | temporarily stores selection in computer memory |
| Edit - Find | locate data on map |
| Edit - Find Again | repeat Edit-Find Command |
| Edit - Edit/Add Station/Object... | add or change station or object on map |
| Edit - Edit/Add Weather Object | add or change weather object on map |
| Edit - Clear Stations and Msgs | delete received station information and messages |
| Settings - Master Mode [S-M] - Normal Ham Operation | configure software for normal APRS operation |
| Settings - Master Mode [S-M] - Weather ONLY | configure software for APRS weather station operation |
| Settings - Station | configure WinAPRS with station parameters |
| Settings - APRS | configure WinAPRS with APRS parameters |
| Settings - Serial port | configure serial port |
| Settings - Select TNC Type | configure software for selected TNC type |

| | |
|---|---|
| Settings - TNC | configure WinAPRS with TNC parameters |
| Settings - Position Report Rate | configure rate of position packet transmissions |
| Settings - Weather | configure WinAPRS with weather station equipment parameters |
| Settings - CallBook DataBase | configure CD-ROM call sign directory |
| Settings - Enable Sound | turn on/off WinAPRS sounds |
| Settings - Open VHF TNC | enable communications with VHF/UHF TNC |
| Settings - Open HF TNC (dual) | enable communications with HF TNC |
| Settings - Open WX port | enable communications with weather station equipment |
| Settings - Open GPS port | enable communications with NMEA/GPS equipment |
| Settings - Open RDF port | enable communications with direction finding equipment |
| Settings - Close TNC | disable communications with TNC |
| Settings - Close All ports | disable communications with all external equipment |
| Settings - TNC Commands - Send Position | transmit beacon packet |
| Settings - TNC Commands - Send Objects | transmit objects packet |
| Settings - TNC Commands - Send Grid-Square Position | transmit Maidenhead grid square packet |
| Settings - TNC Commands - Send Weather Report | transmit weather report packet |
| Settings - TNC Commands - Send RDF Report | transmit direction finding packet |
| Settings - TNC Commands - Send APRS Query | transmit APRS query packet |
| Settings - TNC Commands - Send WX Query | transmit an APRS weather station query packet |
| Settings - TNC Commands - VHF TNC - Re-Initialize TNC | configure VHF/UHF TNC with TNC Settings parameters |
| Settings - TNC Commands - VHF TNC - Exit KISS Mode | force VHF/UHF TNC to quit KISS mode |
| Settings - TNC Commands - VHF TNC - Exit Kantronics Host Mode | force VHF/UHF TNC to quit Kantronics TNC host mode |
| Settings - TNC Commands - VHF TNC - Exit AEA Host Mode | force VHF/UHF TNC to quit AEA TNC host mode |
| Settings - TNC Commands - HF TNC - Re-Initialize TNC | configure HF TNC with TNC Settings parameters |
| Settings - TNC Commands - HF TNC - Exit KISS Mode | force HF TNC to quit KISS mode |
| Settings - TNC Commands - HF TNC - Exit Kantronics Host Mode | force HF TNC to quit Kantronics TNC host mode |
| Settings - TNC Commands - HF TNC - Exit AEA Host Mode | force HF TNC to quit AEA TNC host mode |
| Settings - Send Position | transmit position packet |
| Settings - Send Query | transmit APRS query packet |
| Settings - Send Weather | transmit weather report packet |
| Settings - Send WX Query | transmit an APRS weather station query packet |

| | |
|---|---|
| Logging - Station Logging | turn on/off recording received station data |
| Logging - APRS Logging | turn on/off recording received APRS data |
| Logging - NMEA Logging | turn on/off recording received NMEA/GPS data |
| Logging - Local Weather Logging | turn on/off recording received weather reports |
| Logging - Message Logging | turn on/off recording received messages |
| Logging - Local RDF Logging | turn on/off recording received direction finding data |
| Logging - Stop All Logging | disable recording all received data |
| Map - Display Map Boundaries [M-B] | show perimeters of all selectable maps |
| Map - Map List Window | show all selectable maps |
| Map - | select map for display |
| Display - Home View [D-H] | show current map in its default size |
| Display - Auto Refresh Maps | turn on/off automatic map refreshing function |
| Display - Station Call Signs | turn on/off display of call signs on map |
| Display - Station Icons | turn on/off display of icons on map |
| Display - Map Labels | turn on/off display of labels on map |
| Display - Map Symbols | turn on/off display of symbols on map |
| Display - Station Display Options | select station display options |
| Display - Map Display Options | select map display options |
| Display - Overlays [D-O] | select map overlay |
| Display - Overlays - Display Overlay | select map overlay |
| Display - Overlays - Display Overlay List | show list of available map overlays |
| Display - Overlays - (overlay name) | show selected map overlay(s) |
| Display - Course and Speed | turn on/off display of course and speed vectors of moving objects on map |
| Display - All Stations | turn on/off display of all received stations on map |
| Display - Direct Stations Only | turn on/off display of only directly received stations on map |
| Display - Flagged Stations Only | turn on/off display of only received flagged stations on map |
| Display - Tracked Stations Only | turn on/off display of only received tracked stations on map |
| Display - Weather Stations Only | turn on/off display of only received weather stations on map |
| Display - GridSquare (2 Ltr) | overlay 2-character Maidenhead grid squares on map |
| Display - GridSquare (4 Ltr) | overlay 4-character Maidenhead grid squares on map |

| | |
|---|---|
| Display - Grid Square (6 Ltr) | overlay 6-character Maidenhead grid squares on map |
| Display - Civil Air Patrol Grids | overlay Civil Air Patrol grid squares on map |
| Display - Airports | show location of airports on map |
| Display - Overlay Data | show map overlay data |
| Display - Display Coverage Circles | show circles representing station coverage area |
| Display - Zipcodes | show location of ZIP codes on map |
| Display - Replay Track [D-R] | show course of tracked station on map |
| Lists - New Message | create and transmit new message or bulletin |
| Lists - Message List | show transmitted and received messages and bulletins |
| Lists - Map List | show selectable maps |
| Lists - Station List | show received packet stations |
| Lists - Position List | show received stations' location data |
| Lists - When Heard | show list and graph of times that stations were received |
| Lists - Weather List | show received weather data |
| Lists - Flagged Station Lists | show received flagged stations |
| Lists - Track List | show received tracked station data |
| Lists - Mic Enc List | show received MicEncoder stations' data |
| Lists - RDF List | show received direction finding station data |
| Lists - ProtoPath List | show received stations' unproto path |
| Lists - History List | show all received packets |
| Lists - CallBook List | show CD-ROM call sign directory entries |
| Lists - Icon List | show WinAPRS symbols and icons |
| Lists - Global Label List | show global labels |
| Lists - Airport List | show airports |
| Lists - Internal State | show WinAPRS configuration data |
| Lists - Packet Statistics | show received packet data |
| Lists - Memory Usage | show WinAPRS memory usage per hour |
| Lists - Weather Display | show graphic representing local weather station equipment data |
| Lists - 24hr Weather Charts | show graphic representing local weather data for previous 24 hours |
| Windows - Next Window | deselect active window and select an inactive window |
| Windows - New Map Square | open new map window with default map |

| | |
|---|---|
| Windows - Cascade [W-C] | arrange map windows in a stack |
| Windows - Tile [W-T] | arrange map windows side-by-side |
| Windows - Arrange Icons [W-I] | arrange map icons |
| Windows - Terminal Window | open window for direct communications with TNC |
| Windows - 1 (map name) [W-1] | show (map name) map |
| Windows - New Map Polar | open new map window with polar projection of default map |
| Help - Help contents | show contents of WinAPRS help |
| Help - Help Search | open window for searching help |
| Help - Help Help | show information on how to use help |
| Help - About WinAPRS | show information about WinAPRS |
| [Page Down] | magnify map display |
| [Page Up] | reduce map display |

# About the Author

Stan Horzepa, WA1LOU, first licensed in 1969, is an Amateur Extra Class licensee and an ARRL life member. As former Communications Assistant of the Public Service branch of the ARRL's old Communications Department, Stan edited two editions of the *Repeater Directory* and *Net Directory* and started *QST*'s "FM/RPT" column. After leaving ARRL headquarters, Stan started *QST*'s "On Line" and "Packet Perspective" columns, and became editor of *Gateway: The ARRL Packet-Radio Newsletter.* Stan also wrote two packet radio books for the ARRL, *Your Packet Gateway to Packet Radio* and *Practical Packet Radio,* and currently writes *QST*'s "Digital Dimension" column.

WA1LOU has also contributed to *The ARRL Operating Manual*, *The ARRL Handbook for Radio Amateurs*, and *Operating an Amateur Radio Station*. Besides his Amateur Radio writing achievements, Stan has held a number of ARRL appointments (ASCM, NM, OBS, ORS, OVS) and is the former Section Communications Manager of Connecticut. He also has numerous operating awards including A-1 Operator, BPL, DXCC, Public Service, PSHR, WAC, WAS, The Polska Award, and a Central Radio Club Cosmos silver medal.

Stan lives with his wife Laurie and daughter Hayley in Wolcott, Connecticut on top of Compounce Mountain. He has a BA from the University of Connecticut and a JD from Western New England College. Needless to say, Stan is active on packet radio (mostly 2 meters) and runs an APRS digipeater (WA1LOU-15) on 145.79 MHz 24-hours-a-day. If you connect with Stan, he will gladly tell you what he really thinks about the Internet, the news media, and the demise of Moxie as a New England tradition. If you are not within earshot of WA1LOU, electronic mail can be sent to **stanzepa@nai.net**. Stan's URL is **http://www.tapr.org/~wa1lou.**

**"APRS," by budding artist Hayley Horzepa, who prefers that her dad use the Apple icon rather than the # icon for his APRS digipeater.**

# About The American Radio Relay League

The seed for Amateur Radio was planted in the 1890s, when Guglielmo Marconi began his experiments in wireless telegraphy. Soon he was joined by dozens, then hundreds, of others who were enthusiastic about sending and receiving messages through the air—some with a commercial interest, but others solely out of a love for this new communications medium. The United States government began licensing Amateur Radio operators in 1912.

By 1914, there were thousands of Amateur Radio operators—hams—in the United States. Hiram Percy Maxim, a leading Hartford, Connecticut, inventor and industrialist saw the need for an organization to band together this fledgling group of radio experimenters. In May 1914 he founded the American Radio Relay League (ARRL) to meet that need.

Today ARRL, with more than 170,000 members, is the largest organization of radio amateurs in the United States. The League is a not-for-profit organization that:

- promotes interest in Amateur Radio communications and experimentation
- represents US radio amateurs in legislative matters, and
- maintains fraternalism and a high standard of conduct among Amateur Radio operators.

At League headquarters in the Hartford suburb of Newington, the staff helps serve the needs of members. ARRL is also International Secretariat for the International Amateur Radio Union, which is made up of similar societies in more than 150 countries around the world.

ARRL publishes the monthly journal *QST*, as well as newsletters and many publications covering all aspects of

Amateur Radio. Its headquarters station, W1AW, transmits Morse code practice sessions and bulletins of interest to radio amateurs. The League also coordinates an extensive field organization, which provides technical and other support for radio amateurs as well as communications for public-service activities. In addition, ARRL represents US amateurs with the Federal Communications Commission and other government agencies in the US and abroad.

Membership in ARRL means much more than receiving *QST* each month. In addition to the services already described, ARRL offers membership services on a personal level, such as the ARRL Volunteer Examiner Coordinator Program and a QSL bureau.

Full ARRL membership (available only to licensed radio amateurs in the US) gives you a voice in how the affairs of the organization are governed. League policy is set by a Board of Directors (one from each of 15 Divisions). Each year, half of the ARRL Board of Directors stands for election by the Full Members they represent. The day-to-day operation of ARRL HQ is managed by an Executive Vice President and a Chief Financial Officer.

No matter what aspect of Amateur Radio attracts you, ARRL membership is relevant and important. There would be no Amateur Radio as we know it today were it not for the ARRL. We would be happy to welcome you as a member! (An Amateur Radio license is not required for Associate Membership.) For more information about ARRL and answers to any questions you may have about Amateur Radio, write or call:

ARRL
225 Main Street
Newington CT 06111-1494
(860) 594-0200
Prospective new amateurs call:
800-32-NEW HAM (800-326-3942)
E-mail: **newham@arrl.org**
World Wide Web: **http://www.arrl.org/**

# W1AW schedule

| Pacific | Mtn | Cent | East | Sun | Mon | Tue | Wed | Thu | Fri | Sat |
|---|---|---|---|---|---|---|---|---|---|---|
| 6 am | 7 am | 8 am | 9 am | | | | | Fast Code | Slow Code | |
| 7 am | 8 am | 9 am | 10 am | | | | | Code Bulletin | | |
| 8 am | 9 am | 10 am | 11 am | | | | | Teleprinter Bulletin | | |
| 9 am | 10 am | 11 am | noon | | | | | | | |
| 10 am | 11 am | noon | 1 pm | | Visiting Operator Time | | | | | |
| 11 am | noon | 1 pm | 2 pm | | | | | | | |
| noon | 1 pm | 2 pm | 3 pm | | | | | | | |
| 1 pm | 2 pm | 3 pm | 4 pm | Slow Code | Fast Code | Slow Code | Fast Code | Slow Code | Fast Code | Slow Code |
| 2 pm | 3 pm | 4 pm | 5 pm | Code Bulletin | | | | | | |
| 3 pm | 4 pm | 5 pm | 6 pm | Teleprinter Bulletin | | | | | | |
| 4 pm | 5 pm | 6 pm | 7 pm | Fast Code | Slow Code | Fast Code | Slow Code | Fast Code | Slow Code | Fast Code |
| 5 pm | 6 pm | 7 pm | 8 pm | Code Bulletin | | | | | | |
| 6 pm | 7 pm | 8 pm | 9 pm | Teleprinter Bulletin | | | | | | |
| $6^{45}$ pm | $7^{45}$ pm | $8^{45}$ pm | $9^{45}$ pm | Voice Bulletin | | | | | | |
| 7 pm | 8 pm | 9 pm | 10 pm | Slow Code | Fast Code | Slow Code | Fast Code | Slow Code | Fast Code | Slow Code |
| 8 pm | 9 pm | 10 pm | 11 pm | Code Bulletin | | | | | | |
| 9 pm | 10 pm | 11 pm | Mdnte | Teleprinter Bulletin | | | | | | |
| $9^{45}$ pm | $10^{45}$ pm | $11^{45}$ pm | $12^{45}$ am | Voice Bulletin | | | | | | |

**W1AW's schedule is at the same local time throughout the year. The schedule according to your local time will change if your local time does not have seasonal adjustments that are made at the same time as North American time changes between standard time and daylight time. From the first Sunday in April to the last Sunday in October, UTC = Eastern Time + 4 hours. For the rest of the year, UTC = Eastern Time + 5 hours.**

- **Morse code transmissions:**

**Frequencies are 1.818, 3.5815, 7.0475, 14.0475, 18.0975, 21.0675, 28.0675 and 147.555 MHz.**
**Slow Code = practice sent at 5, $7\frac{1}{2}$, 10, 13 and 15 wpm.**
**Fast Code = practice sent at 35, 30, 25, 20, 15, 13 and 10 wpm.**
**Code practice text is from the pages of *QST*. The source is given at the beginning of each practice session and alternate speeds within each session. For example, "Text is from July 1992 *QST*, pages 9 and 81," indicates that the plain text is from the article**

on page 9 and mixed number/letter groups are from page 81. Code bulletins are sent at 18 wpm. W1AW qualifying runs are sent on the same frequencies as the Morse code transmissions. West Coast qualifying runs are transmitted on approximately 3.590 MHz by W6OWP, with W6ZRJ and AB6YR as alternates. At the beginning of each code practice session, the schedule for the next qualifying run is presented. Underline one minute of the highest speed you copied, certify that your copy was made without aid, and send it to ARRL for grading. Please include your name, call sign (if any) and complete mailing address. Send a 9ξ12-inch SASE for a certificate, or a business-size SASE for an endorsement.

• Teleprinter transmissions:

Frequencies are 3.625, 7.095, 14.095, 18.1025, 21.095, 28.095 and 147.555 MHz.
Bulletins are sent at 45.45-baud Baudot and 100-baud AMTOR, FEC Mode B. 110-baud ASCII will be sent only as time allows. On Tuesdays and Saturdays at 6:30 PM Eastern Time, Keplerian elements for many amateur satellites are sent on the regular teleprinter frequencies.

• Voice transmissions:

Frequencies are 1.855, 3.99, 7.29, 14.29, 18.16, 21.39, 28.59 and 147.555 MHz.

• Miscellanea:

On Fridays, UTC, a DX bulletin replaces the regular bulletins. W1AW is open to visitors during normal operating hours: from 1 PM until 1 AM on Mondays, 9 AM until 1 AM Tuesday through Friday, from 1 PM to 1 AM on Saturdays, and from 3:30 PM to 1 AM on Sundays. FCC licensed amateurs may operate the station from 1 to 4 PM Monday through Saturday. Be sure to bring your current FCC amateur license or a photocopy.

In a communication emergency, monitor W1AW for special bulletins as follows: voice on the hour, teleprinter at 15 minutes past the hour, and CW on the half hour.

Headquarters and W1AW are closed on New Year's Day, President's Day, Good Friday, Memorial Day, Independence Day, Labor Day, Thanksgiving and the following Friday, and Christmas Day.

# Index

A

## E-F-G



## H

## I



## K-L



## M

## N-O



## P

## R



## S

## T

**U-V**



**W**

# Notes

# Notes

# Notes

# Notes

# Notes

**ARRL MEMBERS**

This proof of purchase may be used as a $1.50 credit on your next ARRL purchase. Limit one coupon per new membership, renewal or publication ordered from ARRL Headquarters. No other coupon may be used with this coupon. Validate by entering your membership number from your *QST* label below:

|  |  |  |  |  |  |  |  |  |  |
|---|---|---|---|---|---|---|---|---|---|
|  |  |  |  |  |  |  |  |  |  |

APRS

PROOF OF
PURCHASE

# FEEDBACK

Please use this form to give us your comments on this book and what you'd like to see in future editions. You can also e-mail your comments to us at **pubsfdbk@arrl.org** (publications feedback). In that case, please be sure to include your name, call, e-mail address and the book title and edition in the body of your e-mail message. Also indicate whether or not you are an ARRL member.

Where did you purchase this book?
☐ From ARRL directly ☐ From an ARRL dealer

Is there a dealer who carries ARRL publications within:
☐ 5 miles ☐ 15 miles ☐ 30 miles of your location? ☐ Not sure.

**License class:**
☐ Novice ☐ Technician ☐ Technician with HF privileges
☐ General ☐ Advanced ☐ Extra

---

Name ______________________ ARRL member? ☐ Yes ☐ No

Call Sign ______________

Daytime Phone ( ) ______________ Age ______________

Address ______________________________

City, State/Province, ZIP/Postal Code ______________________

If licensed, how long? ______________

Other hobbies ______________

Occupation ______________

**For ARRL use only** **APRS**
Edition 1 2 3 4 5 6 7 8 9 10 11 12
Printing 2 3 4 5 6 7 8 9 10 11 12

From ______________________________

___________________________________

___________________________________

Please affix postage. Post Office will not deliver without postage.

EDITOR, APRS
AMERICAN RADIO RELAY LEAGUE
225 MAIN STREET
NEWINGTON CT 06111-1494

............................................... please fold and tape ...............................................